Anemia

A Guide to Managing and Living with Anemia

The Essential Guide to Understanding Anemia: The Different Types of Anemia, Symptoms, Diagnosis, and Treatment Options All Included!

By: Frederick Earlstein

Foreword

Anemia is a pretty common condition. You probably have heard someone talk about feeling low on iron. You might have even self-diagnosed anemia just because you're feeling weak or experiencing a consistent loss of appetite.

You may not know that iron deficiency is a serious condition that affects many people. It is the most common type of anemia which is a blood disorder. It means a strict diet and iron supplements for people with severe conditions.

What is anemia? How do you know if you have it? What causes this anemia, and how can you treat it? These will all be answered in this book.

I hope this book will help you to understand what anemia is and how you will be able to prevent and treat it.

Table of Contents

Introduction

Anemia is that state of the body when the blood lacks a certain amount of healthy red blood cells or the hemoglobin (Hb) has very low value. Hemoglobin is responsible for the transportation of oxygen to various parts of the body through our blood. If body has lower value of Hb then required our body will feel fatigue, dizzy and many health-related problems also starts as our body is not getting sufficient amount of oxygen.

Anemia is the most common blood condition all over the world. Women and individuals with chronic diseases are at increased risk of anemia. Important factors to remember are:

Certain types of anemia are hereditary, and infants may be affected from the time of birth.

- Women in the childbearing years are predominantly susceptible to iron-deficiency anemia because of the increased blood supply demands during pregnancy and the blood loss from menstruation.
- Also, the women who give birth to babies leads to many critical situations and the many times babies face mental problems or many other sicknesses

- Moreover, older adults may have a higher risk of developing anemia because of poor diet and other medical conditions.

It is vital to educate yourself about anemia in order to manage it and to prevent serious complications that can become fatal.

Chapter One: Understanding Anemia

Blood circulates throughout the body and performs various functions. It is responsible for delivering oxygen and nutrients into the organs and cells. It can also remove carbon dioxide from the body. Blood is also responsible for transporting hormones in the body which helps in communicating important messages.

The blood works with other body fluids like plasma. Blood is mostly comprised of red blood cells while white blood cells are present in limited number. White blood cells are responsible for defending the body against viruses and bacteria.

What Is Anemia?

Anemia can be simply defined as a blood disorder. It is a state where the hemoglobin levels, the iron component of the red blood cells that carries oxygen, is insufficient and the body has fewer red blood cells. Many factors can cause this to happen. Anemia can be developed over time or it can be inherited.

Cause Of Lack Of Red Blood Cells

The body needs enough hemoglobin and red blood cell in order to produce iron, vitamin B12 and folate. This is also essential in the absorption of other minerals and nutrients. Here are some of the causes of having very few red blood cells:

- Iron deficiency due to poor diet.
- Cancer such as leukemia and lymphoma.

- Toxins acquired through environment and food
- Radiation therapy for cancer patients.
- Autoimmune disorders
- Some medication for arthritis
- Pregnancy and child birth
- Chronic disease such as HIV, AIDS and inflammatory disease can also limit the body's ability to produce red blood cells.

Destruction Of Red Blood Cells

Red blood cells can be destroyed even before they reach the end of their normal lifespan which is about 120 days. Sometimes too many red blood cells are destroyed that the bone marrow cannot quickly replace them.

Disease and infection such as lupus or hepatitis can cause the premature destruction of cells. Inherited conditions can also destroy red blood cells in the body. Genetic disorders such as autoimmune disorders cause the body to make antibodies which are proteins in the immune system. These antibodies destroy red blood cells early. A person can also lose red blood cells when they lack the enzyme glucose-6-phosphate dehydrogenase. Red blood cells usually break apart faster if the body does not have this enzyme.

Losing Too Many Red Blood Cells

The third most common way for people to develop anemia is through blood loss. Severe blood loss can also lead to low iron levels in the body. Without iron, the body is unable to create sufficient red blood cells and the cells that the body is able to create contain less hemoglobin. Heavy menstrual bleeding can cause excessive blood loss for women. Ulcers and bleeding in the digestive tract can also cause anemia.

Other Types of Anemia

Anemia sadly affects more than 30% of the world's population. According to WHO, 42% of children below 5 and 40% of pregnant women globally are anemic. More than two billion people globally and over three million Americans have anemia.

An anemic person does not have enough red blood cells in their body. While the drop in red blood cells could result from different reasons, iron deficiency anemia is the most common type of anemia. However, there are other types.

Iron deficiency anemia might be the only type of anemia that you know. But, other types can be inherited or acquired. Let's examine some of these other types of anemia.

- **Hemolytic Anemia**

This anemia results from acquired or inherited diseases. The diseases cause deformed red blood cells, making them easily destroyed in tight spaces such as capillaries, reducing their life span.

Sickle cell anemia is one of the genetic forms of this condition.

- **Sickle Cell Anemia**

Individuals with this genetic anemia have abnormal sickle-shaped red blood cells with hemoglobin S. Red blood cells should normally be bi-concave. The sickle-shaped cells cause low oxygen tension in the tissues, making the individual feel pain.

- **Aplastic Anemia**

This anemia results from a malfunction of bone marrows, causing inadequate production of red blood cells. This condition can be congenital (from birth) or acquired (radiation and other chemicals like insecticides). It is also called bone marrow aplasia (failure).

- **Megaloblastic Anemia**

This anemia is caused by folic acid, intrinsic factor, and vitamin B12 deficiency leading to the slow development of erythroblasts in the bone marrow. These red blood cells are called "megaloblasts" as they are large with odd shapes.

- **Pernicious Anemia**

Pernicious anemia is strictly caused by a lack of intrinsic factor which allows for the absorption of vitamin B12. The lack of vitamin B12 makes it impossible to develop healthy red blood cells.

You might have noted that these types of anemia are either inherited or acquired. They are all also caused by one factor or the other.

Diagnosis of Anemia

Now that you know some of the basics about what anemia is and how it can affect you, you may be ready to learn more about how it is diagnosed. In this section, you will learn the basic tests that doctors use to diagnose anemia. If you think you or a loved one may have this condition, it will be important for you to know what process your doctor will go through to make the diagnosis.

1.) Medical/Family History

The first thing any doctor should do is take a detailed medical and family history.

Many medical conditions – including some forms of anemia – are hereditary, so it is important to know whether the condition runs in your family. While taking your medical history, your doctor may ask you if you have experienced any of the common signs and symptoms of anemia. He may also ask about conditions that have been linked to or known to cause anemia.

During the medical history portion of your exam, it is important that you give your doctor all the details he needs. There may be things that you do not think are relevant but could actually help your doctor make a diagnosis or at least influence his chosen course of treatment. Be sure to let your doctor know about any medications you are taking and if you have made any recent changes to your diet or lifestyle.

2.) Physical Exam

The next step your doctor will take is to perform a physical exam. Depending on your symptoms, your doctor may perform certain tests. Few of the tests the doctor may perform include:

- Listening to your heart for an arrhythmia
- Feeling your abdomen to check your liver and spleen
- Listening to your lungs for abnormal breathing

In cases of severe blood loss, your doctor may even perform a pelvic or rectal exam to look for sources of bleeding.

3.) Blood Tests

When it comes to diagnosing anemia, the first test your doctor is likely to perform is a complete blood count (CBC). A complete blood count measures many different parts of your blood and returns a series of numbers. These numbers are then checked against reference values to determine whether your values are within the normal range.

Some of the things a CBC tests for include:

- Hemoglobin levels
- Hematocrit levels
- Red blood cell count
- White blood cell count
- Platelet levels
- Mean corpuscular volume (MCV)

Hemoglobin is a type of iron-rich protein that is found in your blood – it is essential for helping to carry oxygen throughout your body. A hematocrit test is used to determine how much space your red blood cells take up in your blood.

In other words, a hematocrit test measures the volume of your red blood cells. If either of these tests returns lower than normal results, it could be a sign of anemia.

Abnormal levels of red blood cells, white blood cells or platelets may also be an indication of anemia. It is important to take into account racial and ethnic norms, however, because some people may have different "normal" levels than others.

The final aspect of a CBC, the mean corpuscular volume, measures the average size of your red blood cells. If they are abnormally small, it could be sign of anemia or another blood condition.

4.) Other Tests Used

If the results of your CBC suggest that you may have anemia, your doctor is likely to perform other tests to confirm the diagnosis. Some of these tests may include hemoglobin electrophoresis, a reticulocyte count and iron levels. These tests will not only help to confirm whether or not you have anemia, but perhaps what type you have.

Hemoglobin electrophoresis is a test that measures the various types of hemoglobin in the blood. This will help identify which type of anemia you have. A reticulocyte count measures the number of new blood cells in your blood – this can help to determine whether your bone marrow is producing blood cells at a healthy rate. Testing for iron levels in the blood and body will assist to identify or rule out iron-deficiency anemia.

Anemia can be caused by or linked to a variety of other conditions including lead poisoning, vitamin deficiencies, or kidney failure. In instances where anemia might be due to blood loss, your doctor could suggest extra tests to detect the source of the bleeding. With these tests, you may need to take a kit home then return samples to the lab. In extreme cases, a bone marrow test may be needed.

Chapter Two: Role of Iron In The Body

Why Iron Is The Most Important Element In The Body?

Iron produces red blood cells (RBCs) in our body

The red hue of blood is due to the presence of iron in it. Iron is normally transported to the bone marrow, where it produces hemoglobin.

There is a chain reaction regarding how iron works in the body. The lifespan of red blood cells is 120 days, after which, they break down and release the iron which is recycled again to produce red blood cells. This is how important iron is for the body.

However, on daily basis, 1 - 2 mg of iron is also lost from the body, due to shedding of skin cells and shedding of cells inside the gastrointestinal tract due to blood loss. Women lose more iron than men because of the menstruation process.

Transports oxygen:

Iron in the blood helps transport oxygen to all parts of the body. Lack of iron can cause oxygen deprivation and effect multiple organs in the body, causing cell death too, which can lead to heart failure and death.

Muscle function:

Besides red blood cells, iron also produces a protein called Myoglobin. This protein binds to the oxygen in the muscles and helps transport it to muscle tissue for proper muscle movement. Lack of iron can cause muscle weakness and severe pain because oxygen doesn't reach all the muscle tissue.

Boosts metabolism

6 % of iron is found in various enzymes in the body that aids in respiration, and in metabolizing energy. It also helps in synthesis of neurotransmitters, collagen, and improve the working mechanism of the immune system.

Not many people know that iron has a role to play in the metabolism, too. When someone lacks iron, the process of converting glucose into energy is affected and slowed down. Besides lack of iron, this signals the body that there is a lack of insulin, too. Hence, the body begins to produce more insulin to make up the insulin deficiency. This combination of high insulin levels and low iron contributes to obesity because metabolism is largely affected.

Higher levels of insulin can also cause diseases like Diabetes-2.

Keeps diseases at bay

Iron is one of those nutrients that helps reduce the risk of developing certain diseases. Presence of iron in the right amount produces two oxidants called, peroxidase and catalase. These two help strengthen the immune system and keep diseases at bay. Lack of iron causes the immune system to become weaker and a person can be susceptible to certain diseases.

What Is The Normal Range Of Iron In The Body?

25 % of the iron in the body is stored as ferritin in the liver, spleen, and bone marrow, while some is found in the blood circulating in the body.

An adult male has around 1000 mg of stored iron, which is enough for about three years. However, women only have about 300 mg of stored iron, which is enough for about six months.

What Happens If Iron Content Is Low In The Body?

Iron depletion takes place when the body doesn't get enough iron. It causes the stored iron to deplete. Further decreases can cause iron-deficient erythropoiesis or even iron deficiency anemia if the iron content becomes too low.

The brain and immune system are largely affected when iron content is low in the body. This is because oxygen doesn't reach all the organs, tissue, and cells properly and causes poor brain functionality and infections.

Fatigue is common among people who are iron deficient. They are easily exhausted, without performing any heavy activity.

Pregnant women who are iron deficient, may experience premature birth where the baby could be smaller in size than normal babies. Around 740 mg of iron is lost during delivery. Other than that, breastfeeding a child also causes iron deficiency in mothers. Breastfeeding increases the iron intake requirement by 1 mg per day.

Numerous other body parts are also affected when there is a lack of iron in the body. Dry skin, poor hair quality, and brittle nails are common conditions experienced by people who are iron deficient.

People who frequently donate blood may also experience iron deficiency if they follow a diet that lacks enough iron. A person who donates blood loses an average of 200 – 250 mg of iron per donation.

What Happens If The Body Stores Too Much Iron?

The iron we get from our diet is either consumed immediately or stored for later use. It is used immediately when our iron intake is low, but when we consume more than the required amount, it is stored in the body.

The stored amount can cause iron toxicity; a condition where stored iron is deposited in tissues of the heart and liver. It damages the functionality of these two organs and inflicts damage on muscle tissues as well could result in death.

The bottom line is that both too little of iron, and too much iron is dangerous. One should intake the recommended amount to stay healthy.

Important Facts To Know About Iron

- Iron is a mineral found in every cell of the body. It provides the red hue to the blood, and also gives red blood cells the strength to transport oxygen to all the organs in the body.
- Lack of iron can wreak havoc in the body. An iron deficiency is called anemia, and can cause many organs to function improperly or not function at all. Anemia also weakens the protective barrier that

keeps infections away. Other than that, slow cognitive development, difficulty in maintaining body temperature, poor metabolism, breathlessness, weak muscles, and fatigue are just some of the many problems a person can face when lacking iron.

- Pregnant women are the most prone to losing iron from their bodies. They lose it through giving birth. Anemia during pregnancy is said to increase the chances of delivering a premature birth.
- Babies can be unhealthy, and could be born with health issues. The rate of survival could also be reduced within the first year.
- In toddlers, lack of iron can affect the motor functions and make them slower, thinking skills are affected, too. Some children may have a tough time understanding and speaking. In teens, it can weaken memory, and reduce other mental functions.
- Girls and women of childbearing age require higher amounts of iron in their body as they lose blood in the process of menstruation.
- Breast milk does not provide as good a source of iron once the baby reaches six months old. This is the stage when the baby should be given iron-fortified foods or cereals containing iron.

- Absorbing iron can be a daunting task, especially in case of plant foods. Taking a diet that's rich in iron and consuming foods that are rich in vitamin C can increase iron absorption.
- There are two types of iron that can be attained through eating. Heme iron and non-heme iron. Heme iron is obtained from animal protein, such as seafood, fish, poultry, and meat. While non-heme iron is obtained from plant foods, such as vegetables, fruits, grains, nuts, seeds, and beans.
- During pregnancy, a woman's body requires more iron than normal. Here is where iron supplement, along with prenatal vitamins is recommended to make up for iron deficiency. While plant foods contain more iron, they are not easily absorbed compared to iron found in meat.
- Iron absorption rate ranges from 5 % to 35 %. However, for individuals who are pure vegetarians, it can be difficult to fulfill the iron requirement because plant foods provide non-heme iron, which is not easily absorbed. Taking vitamin C excessively can help in this case because it helps in the iron absorption. This way, vegetarians can keep their iron levels balanced.
- To reduce the phytate content, vitamin C enhances this effect. Sprinkling sunflower seeds, or roasted

nuts, or sprouts can increase vitamin C content in a diet, especially a plant diet; making it easier to absorb iron.

- Foods like whole grains, tea, nuts, legumes, soy, and seeds contain a natural chemical called phytates. This chemical is mostly found on the outer covering of these foods and interferes with iron absorption in the body. People who eat these foods in their daily diet may face a challenge to absorb it properly.
- Iron consumption is one thing and iron absorption is another. Consuming iron on daily basis isn't enough, you need to make sure it is also absorbed into the bloodstream. Iron absorption is essential because it accounts for immediate use and storage purposes. If iron isn't being absorbed quickly, ferritin, which is a protein that stores iron supply, is depleted. Complete depletion may cause anemia. Therefore, iron absorption is as important as consuming it.
- Avoid drinking tea, coffee, herbal tea, and black tea before eating. Why? These drinks contain a substance called polyphenol, which suppresses iron absorption. All the iron-rich foods you eat after consuming any of these teas can become difficult to absorb, and you may not receive the daily iron

content your body requires. You can drink tea or coffee after an hour, so iron has had time to get absorbed in the bloodstream.

- There are many diseases that can cause iron deficiency. These include kidney failure, coeliac disease; intestinal reaction towards gluten, menorrhagia; heavy periods, bowel cancer; gut bleeding, stomach ulcers, and chronic malabsorption.
- People who are consistent blood donors are at a high risk of being iron deficient. These people need to consume a diet that is heavy on iron intake.
- Iron deficiency can restrict your body to make new blood as well. Iron is one of the most important minerals that helps in the formation of hemoglobin; a deficiency can cause problems producing enough hemoglobin for the body.
- Besides being important for brain activities, iron is also important for muscle health. Contraction of muscles takes place when iron present in the muscle tissues supply oxygen to all the muscle tissues. If your muscles are losing their elastic nature and tone, then you may be suffering from anemia.
- A weaker, slow working brain is due to iron deficiency. One of the major roles of iron in the

body is to supply oxygen blood to the brain, make sure it functions properly. Our brain uses only 20% of the oxygen, which is why iron is crucial for working of the brain. Without consistent oxygen flow in the brain, the cognitive system is affected and can trigger conditions like dementia and Alzheimer's.

- Muscle spasms are common for people lacking iron in their body; oxygen not reaching all the parts of the body and preventing muscles to contract due to low levels of blood and oxygen. Things can get worse when iron content drops drastically and can cause restless leg syndrome.
- The ability of our bodies to regulate temperature is due to iron present in our blood. This means that iron in our body helps regulate body temperature. If you are feeling too cold or too hot then you might be running low on iron.
- Taking the recommended amount of iron aids in treating chronic disorders such as anemia, renal failure, and various intestinal diseases. It also covers up for the amount of blood lost in a condition by helping produce hemoglobin in the body.
- It is iron that helps in the synthesizing process of a number of important chemicals in the brain that

helps us be in a good mood. These include serotonin, dopamine, and norepinephrine. These chemicals play a vital role in brain functionality and are responsible for getting a better sleep, sexual desire, and ability to fight depression.

- Iron plays a fundamental role in triggering the healing process that occurs in the body. It strengthens the immune system and helps ward off diseases.
- Less red blood cells count can cause the blood pressure to fluctuate and cause a number of problems including insomnia. Iron helps in treating insomnia by regulating circadian rhythm. Circadian rhythm disorder is common in people who lack iron because it disrupts their sleep-wake cycle. These people may feel sleepy in daytime and have a tough time sleeping at night. Also, suffering from depression for no reason at all is also common when iron is lacking in the body.

Chapter Three: Iron-Deficiency Anemia

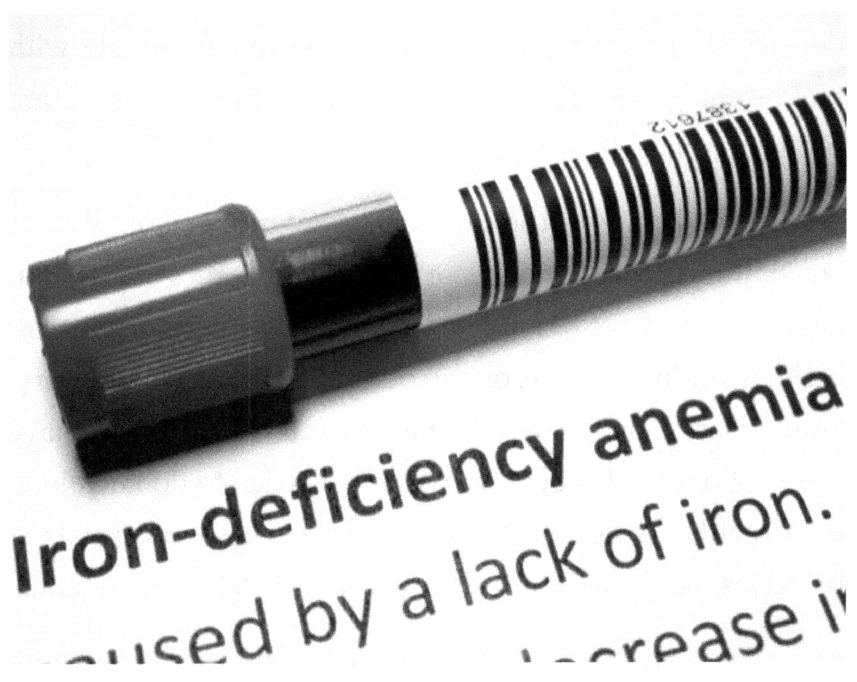

How Does Iron Deficiency Happen?

Unfortunately, iron deficiency is one of the most common vitamin and mineral deficiencies known to North America. It is a very easy thing to miss, and its importance is rarely stressed when nutrition is discussed. However, having a lack of hemoglobin in the body can be very dangerous to our mental and physical functioning.

Sometimes, we might develop an iron deficiency because we have a unique hemoglobin structure. When our hemoglobin structures are abnormal, this can lead to a deficiency of iron in our blood. For example, people with thalassemia and sickle cell anemia may find that they are prone to iron deficiencies.

Another way iron deficiencies might develop is if we are in unfortunate accidents or have health issues that lead to a large quantity of blood lost. We may lose blood from a car accident, kidney failure, or any other type of traumatic injury. Sometimes, it isn't an accident at all, and the reason we have lost a lot of blood is because we have chosen to donate blood on a regular basis. Whatever the reason, large quantities of blood loss can be a significant cause of iron deficiency anemia.

Women who are pregnant and young women with heavy periods are also at high risk. Pregnant women, in particular, are vulnerable as their bodies go through a series of physical changes, including assigning blood to the uterus, where they use it to support the growth of the babies inside of them. But as mentioned previously, that makes it all the more important to have hemoglobin levels as close to normal as possible.

Sometimes, we simply have a difficult time absorbing iron, no matter how much we eat. When this is the case, it is often due to health problems or gastrointestinal surgeries. For example, people with celiac disease often have only a restricted amount of iron that the body is able to absorb at one time.

Cancer can also be a cause of iron deficiency. When red blood cell synthesis is suppressed by drugs that are a part of chemotherapy treatments or bone marrow is replaced by cancerous cells, these can both deplete iron in the system. It's an unfortunate result of an already heart-wrenching disease.

Another issue that can lead to iron deficiency anemia is internal bleeding. It sounds very scary, and indeed can be. Things like ulcers and polyps are common causes of internal bleeding. Anemia can also occur if over-the-counter pain medications like aspirin are frequently used. Unfortunately, while they promise to help us feel better, a common side effect of using these "medications" is bleeding in the stomach. Uterine fibroids have also been diagnosed as a cause of iron deficiency anemia. When these fibroids develop, they can cause intense pain in the abdomen and a heavy menstrual flow, which has also been linked to anemia.

Finally, and possibly most commonly, an inadequate diet can be the result of iron deficiency. If the body doesn't receive enough vitamin B12, folate, or iron, it can make it very difficult for iron to remain in the body or be absorbed and utilized for its proper function.

Symptoms of Iron Deficiency

Sometimes we don't realize there is a problem until it is too late. However, if we are diligent, it is possible to catch warning signs of iron deficiency before they turn too serious. Regardless, iron deficiency is an affliction that can be treated with relative ease by incorporating lifestyle changes that make it easier for our bodies to receive and absorb iron. Here are some signs and symptoms of iron deficiency to look out for.

- Lethargy
- Fatigue
- Less effective immune system functioning
- Inflammation of the tongue
- Fluctuations in body temperature
- Fragile finger and toe nails
- Decreased performance, whether at school or work
- Slow brain development
- Pale skin
- Strange or weird cravings, such as the desire to eat dirt
- Irregular heartbeat
- Shortness of breath
- Strange creeping feelings in the legs
- Swelling of the tongue
- Sore tongue

- Difficulty in warming extremities, such as hands and feet
- Decreased cognitive functioning
- Difficulties in doing physical work
- Memory loss and decreased function of the memory
- Decreased mental functions

As you can tell, these can be serious issues that should be tended to at once. This is especially true if pregnant. Mothers with iron deficiencies have a greater chance of giving birth to small babies with lower life expectancies.

Symptoms of Excess Iron

Getting too much iron is usually not an issue that most people talk often about. Usually, anemia is the star of the show when it comes to conversations about iron. However, it is possible for excess iron to build up in the system, and once a person reaches the age of 40 and above, complications from built up iron in the system may surface.

Symptoms of excess iron, although subtle, may be noted early. These symptoms include:

- Incontinence or frequent urination
- Joint pain
- Fatigue
- Lethargy

- Tiredness
- Weight loss
- Difficulty performing physical work

If symptoms of excess iron are caught early, you may be diagnosed with excess iron in the blood, a condition known as hemochromatosis.

Iron Deficiency and Mental Health

Sometimes we may have an iron deficiency and don't even know it. This can cause mental responses to our deficiency that may otherwise be attributed to external factors and irritants when in reality, it is a lack of iron that is contributing to these health problems.

Mental and emotional complications of low iron in the body are often overlooked. However, iron deficiency can often contribute to depression, anxiety, and other difficulties in mental functioning. If you are not receiving enough iron, or your body isn't absorbing iron properly, you may be at risk.

The following are some of the mental and emotional complications that can be associated with an iron deficiency:

- Depression
- Anxiety

- Irritability
- Extreme fatigue
- Appetite loss
- Panic attacks
- Insomnia
- Chest tightness
- Irregular heartbeat
- Mood swings
- Helplessness
- Sadness
- Irregular heart rhythms
- Visual disturbances
- Headaches
- Feelings of dread
- Preoccupation with death or dying
- Muscle weakness
- Issues swallowing/choking
- Restless leg syndrome
- Feelings of unsteadiness/vertigo
- Dizziness
- Motion sickness
- Inability to focus
- Difficulty reading and concentrating
- Difficulty completing simple tasks
- Stress

Overall, the mental toll that an iron deficiency can have on the body is extreme. It can be very frustrating to live with the physical and mental symptoms of an iron deficiency. If you suspect you have low iron, visit a doctor as soon as possible, or continue reading on to find ways to remedy this affliction and begin to turn your life around to get back on track as soon as possible.

Iron Deficiency Anemia: What It Is and How to Cope With and Prevent It

Iron deficiency anemia is the specific title for people whose bodies are lacking in red blood cells and hemoglobin because of an iron deficiency. This particular ailment is the most common anemia issue and can sometimes be brought on by decisions that we make on a daily basis. Little things, like the choices we make in our diet, can play a big role when it comes to our health, and we often don't realize just how much power we have over how we feel.

Sometimes the cause of iron deficiency anemia can be simple, such as heavy blood loss during a woman's menstrual cycle. Women who experience blood loss during pregnancy may also develop this specific type of anemia.

For the most part, iron deficiency anemia is not a life-threatening condition. Despite that, there are many forms of anemia that require special attention. Regardless of the fact that a slight iron deficiency is not considered harmful, many people don't realize that they are suffering from this condition and when left untreated it can become dangerous. Because of the important function of iron, if hemoglobin is decreased in the red blood cells, it means that the heart has to work harder in order to distribute oxygen throughout the body.

Unfortunately, this can lead to an irregular heartbeat in some cases or an enlarged heart in others. Both of these pose a serious health risk and if left untreated, they can even cause heart failure to occur. This is when an iron deficiency goes from being inconvenient to being lethal.

Causes of Iron Deficiency Anemia

Iron deficiency is caused by a lack of iron in the body, but there are different underlying reasons why you might have a deficient iron level. Some of the reasons why you might have low iron levels include:

Inadequate Diet

If you are not eating enough meals with iron, it can result in iron deficiency anemia. Foods like meat, eggs, and green vegetables are rich in the iron content that your body needs.

The exclusion of most of these foods in a vegetarian's diet is why they suffer from iron deficiency more than others. However, there are vegetables that a vegetarian can take to maintain the iron balance.

Don't go on a diet without ensuring all the nutrients your body needs are provided. As a man between 19 and 50, you need at least 8 milligrams of iron daily. Women from 50 years and younger need at least 18 milligrams daily. Pregnant women need as much as 27 mg of iron. You can consult a nutritionist if you're not sure your diet has adequate iron.

Internal Blood Loss

Some medical conditions cause internal bleeding and this loss of blood results in a drop in iron levels. These conditions include colon cancer, stomach ulcer, hernia, colon polyps, and uterine fibroids. Regular use of some pain relievers like aspirin can cause stomach bleeding, which leads to iron deficiency.

Pregnancy

Pregnant women need more oxygen for the baby. There is also an increased blood volume which demands more iron. If the pregnant woman's diet is not adjusted accordingly, it can lead to iron-deficiency anemia.

Heavy Menstruation

People with heavy menstruation often lose a lot of blood, resulting in iron deficiency. The blood loss could also be a result of endometriosis. Some people don't know that they even have it. You can resolve this iron deficiency by treating the underlying causes using birth control pills or devices.

Slow Absorption of Iron

Due to conditions like celiac disease, Crohn's disease, or ulcerative colitis, your body might find it hard to absorb iron from your small intestine meals. In this case, it is not a matter of taking enough iron but the inability of your body to absorb it. Surgeries like a gastric bypass can also demand the removal of parts of the intestine, making it harder for your body to absorb iron.

Genetic conditions and injuries which cause a lot of blood loss can also lead to iron deficiency in the body. If you have any of these causes, you might want to check for symptoms of iron deficiency.

Who is at Risk?

From the causes, it is clear that women are more likely to suffer from this deficiency. They have a higher need for iron daily and even more when pregnant or menstruating.

This figure doesn't mean that men and children don't get iron deficient. People at risk of having iron deficiency include:

- Premature or low weight babies
- Children going through a growth spurt
- Blood donors
- People with a family history of anemia
- Women with reproductive years
- People with intestinal disorders and chronic illnesses
- Vegetarians

You belong to a group of people at risk of iron deficiency doesn't mean you have the condition.

If you think you are low on iron, you can watch out for symptoms.

How to Prevent Iron Deficiency Anemia

It is possible that if you are reading this book, you are already suffering from iron deficiency anemia. Whether or not you have already been diagnosed with anemia or you are simply worried about living a lifestyle that is low in iron, there are ways that you can make sure to prevent iron deficiency anemia from happening to you, or getting worse if it already has happened.

The first way to prevent iron deficiency anemia seems fairly intuitive. Simply eat more iron. There is a section in this book entirely dedicated to iron-rich foods. Try incorporating these foods into your diet on a daily basis and you will be closer to preventing anemia from happening to you or worsening.

The second way to prevent iron deficiency anemia is to eat foods that support the absorption of iron. Whether we are eating enough iron or not, there are other factors at play when it comes to the absorption of iron in our bodies. If our bodies aren't capable of absorbing enough iron, that comes down to the foods that we are eating and the other nutrients we may be deficient in, such as B12 and folates. This is especially common in vegan and vegetarian diets. Learning more about foods that support iron absorption in the body is key.

The third way to ensure that iron deficiency anemia passes you by is to combine consuming iron with eating vitamin C. Vitamin C is one of the many nutrients that our bodies need a healthy supply of, and this is very evident when it comes to the absorption of iron. Eating iron-rich foods, such as spinach, with vitamin C-rich foods, such as oranges, is a great way to make sure that our bodies are ready to absorb the iron that we give it.

What to Do When Diagnosed With Iron Deficiency Anemia

Living with any kind of medical problem can be very difficult, especially when these issues require changes to be made to our daily routines and diets. Unfortunately, that is always going to be the case when our bodies are lacking in vitamins and nutrients. Without these nutrients, our bodies will gradually grow weaker and complications may arise.

When you are officially diagnosed with iron deficiency anemia, it is important to get a good idea of the scope of the problem. If you have been living on a diet that is severely lacking in iron for several years, complications may arise from that, and these complications should be dealt with through medical attention. Do not attempt to self-treat iron deficiency anemia, as we are all different and our bodies require specific vitamins and minerals to function properly.

If you are diagnosed with iron deficiency anemia, there are a few steps that you should take immediately. The first is to speak with your doctor about appropriate supplements, not only for iron but for vitamin B12 and folates as well, as these deficiencies are often found alongside the iron deficiency and come hand-in-hand. Once you have discussed the proper supplementation that is right for you, then you are going to be responsible for improving your diet and making sure that you are getting enough vitamins and minerals to maintain a healthy lifestyle.

It is very important that you learn as much about the specific type of anemia that you have. Be open and honest with your doctors, as they will often withhold treatment until they have pinpointed the underlying cause of your ailment. When they have a good idea of what is causing your issues, only then will they feel comfortable deciding upon a line of action to help you to treat your iron deficiency.

When to Consult a Doctor

Unfortunately, anemia that can be fixed and prevented purely through the diet is not the only type of anemia that can develop. While the suggestions mentioned above are great ways to help iron enter the body, there are some times when medical intervention is required to treat your specific type of anemia.

While diet is a crucial factor in living with anemia, there are times when your specific medical needs will not be fixed by diet alone. For example, those with celiac disease or other gastrointestinal diseases will need the help of a doctor to get proper nutrition.

Other types of anemia that should be dealt with by an experienced medical care practitioner who is well-educated on your specific case include Crohn's disease, aplastic anemia, cancer-induced anemia, and hemolytic anemia. All of these forms of anemia require medical attention and the information in this book should not be used as a substitute for responsible medical advice.

Treating Iron Deficiency

Treating iron deficiency is possible and easy but it is vital to diagnose the cause first. One type of treatment is not suitable for different causes of anemia and each needs to be approached differently.

Normally, there are 3 causes that can cause iron deficiency:

- Compromised red blood cells production.
- Blood loss.
- Red blood cells damage within the blood.

The treatment for each type is carried out differently.

Your doctor may not treat your anemia until the cause of lack of iron is diagnosed. Also, using a treatment that is not suitable for the kind of anemia a person has can have disastrous outcomes, therefore, diagnosing the cause is highly important.

Caused By Blood Loss

There can be many reasons for losing large volume of blood, such as getting into accidents, sustaining injuries, surgeries, stomach diseases, internal bleeding, and menstruation in women.

When you lose a lot of blood, the doctor might treat you in one of the following ways:

- Blood transfusion.
- Oxygen transfusion.
- Treatment with fluids.
- Iron supplements.

In case a wound is fresh and the bleeding hasn't stopped, the doctor will first identify the cause and source of bleeding, take steps to stop it, and provide treatment after that.

Caused By Decreased Red Blood Cell Production

The kind of treatment you receive is based on the cause of decreased red blood cell production:

Anemia caused by iron deficiency: The body fails to produce red blood cells if there is a lack of iron in the body. It is not much of a problem to determine the cause of decreased red blood cells among women, who are still menstruating, because it is an obvious source of blood loss. However, men and women who have a poor red blood cell production need to go through a colonoscopy or barium enema to determine the cause.

The most common form of treatment that doctors offer in case of iron deficiency anemia is iron supplements that contain the ferrous form of iron in them as they are easy to absorb.

While a two-tablet serving of iron supplement can provide a person with 54mg of carbonyl iron, it may not the best cup of tea. Why? Because iron supplements need to be consumed with precautions or else, they may cause further problems.

People with weak digestive systems find it daunting to consume iron supplements, as they are absorbed in the upper part of the digestive system.

If you are looking forward to iron supplements as treatment for iron deficiency, you need to take the following precautions:

- Never take iron supplements without consulting with a doctor. Firstly, you don't know what dosage is safe for you. You might consume a heavier dose and exacerbate the problem rather than treat it. Taking iron supplements in excess can cause high fatigue, diarrhea, vomiting, heart disease, irritability, joint pain, headaches.
- Iron supplements recommended to an adult do not work for children. Never let a child consume the supplement, or it might cause iron poisoning. It can be fatal, or damage internal organs of a child in a matter of hours. The symptoms of iron poisoning include

nausea, vomiting, diarrhea, and dizziness. One must seek immediate medical attention if iron poisoning is suspected.

- Iron supplements are one of the best solutions to treat iron deficiency but they can cause side effects in some people if they are not careful. Iron supplements should never be taken on an empty stomach, always with food.

  They should not be continued for more than a year without consulting a physician. If you experience stomach aches, diarrhea, nausea, or constipation, then you might be facing the side effects when taken on an empty stomach or in excessive amounts. Another reason for experiencing side effects, the iron supplement could be too strong for you. Discuss with your physician, and possibly opt for a different formula that your body can tolerate.

- Do not take multiple supplements together. If the doctor has prescribed you to take both calcium and iron supplements then never take them together. This is because calcium makes it difficult to absorb iron and can create issues. Set a different time to consume both if required.
- It is better to consume iron supplements with something that is mildly acidic and contains vitamin C.

Many doctors advise people to take iron supplements along with orange juice as it contains vitamin C. This is because vitamin C helps in the absorption of iron.

Your doctor may also recommend to eat iron-rich foods along with iron supplements. These include beans, meat, egg yolks, whole grains, nuts, seeds, dairy, and seafood.

After you have taken iron supplements for a few months, your doctor will check your iron levels; hemoglobin, ferritin, and hematocrit, if there is no improvement and the red blood cell count is still low then it may be possible that you are suffering from a severe case of anemia and need to opt for a different treatment.

If taking iron orally isn't a choice, the doctor might prescribe iron injections which are injected into a vein.

In case of a life-threatening situation, blood transfusion is given the highest priority because of lack of blood in the body.

Caused By Increased Red Blood Cell Destruction

Hemolytic anemia is a condition in which red blood cells are destroyed and removed from the bloodstream either in the vessels or anywhere in the body. This not only leads to iron deficiency because the production of red blood cells is compromised but a number of other serious problems as well.

When the red blood cells begin to break down in the body or destroyed in the spleen, it causes the iron in the hemoglobin to accumulate is several places and cause organ damage on a large scale.

The symptoms include paleness, fever, weakness, dizziness, etc. If these symptoms are mild and next to none, then a treatment may not be required as red blood cell destruction won't be that high.

Iron accumulation in the body needs to be stopped immediately. People with severe cases of hemolytic anemia require surgery to replace faulty heart valves, formations of tumor, and to repair blood vessels that have sustained damage.

Other treatments include blood transfusions, steroids that can stop the body from attacking the immune system and destroying its own red blood cells.

In case these treatments do not work, the last resort is to go for a splenectomy; removal of spleen via surgery. This is because it starts within the spleen. It should be noted that people can lead a normal life without their spleen.

Coping With Iron Deficiency Anemia

Depending on how far along it is, the typical understanding is that anemia is something that can be easily treated. However, complications from long-term anemia can be a little bit more dangerous, such as heart growth or irregular heartbeats.

Fortunately, most people catch anemia early on, and coping with it can be easy. Most of the time, supplements will be involved, and their necessity may last anywhere from a few months to a year or more, depending on what your doctor recommends. It is important to follow instructions and pay close attention to any symptoms that the iron supplements you are taking cause you to have, as it can become dangerous to put too much iron in the body.

When you are taking supplements, make sure to regularly consult with your doctor and ask to change the supplements if you find yourself suffering from gastrointestinal distress or other side effects from the supplements. While you are taking the supplements, try to get into the habit of eating iron-rich foods and foods that will support the absorption of iron in your system.

Listen carefully to any orders and recommendations given to you by your doctor and follow them until you are in the clear. In some cases, you may end up needing to receive blood or an IV to help deal with severe iron deficiency. Iron deficiency anemia isn't always a serious problem, but when it persists for too long, complications may become severe. Do whatever is necessary to overcome these obstacles and balance out your deficiency once and for all.

Chapter Four: Sickle Cell Anemia

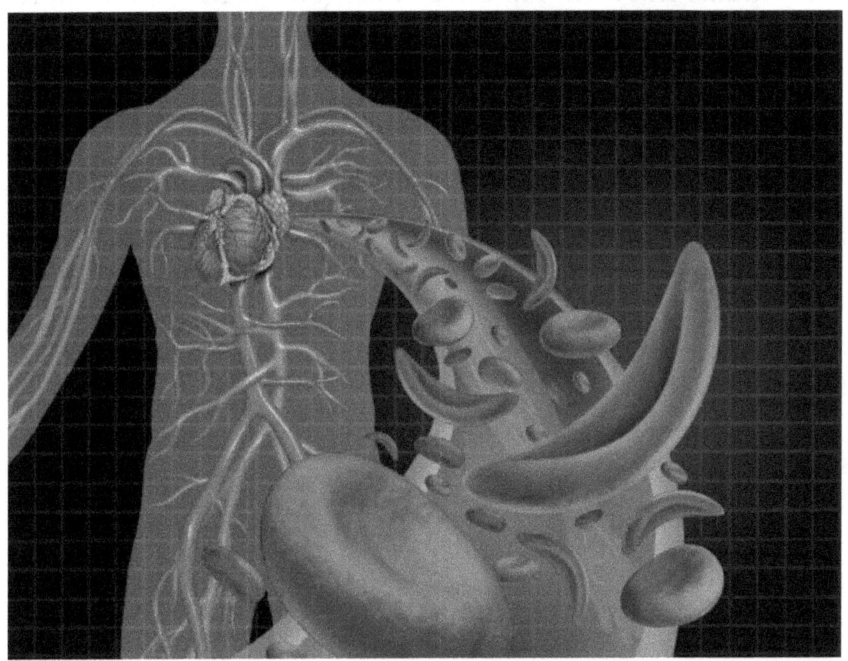

History of the Disease

Sickle cell disease is a collection of symptoms and diseases that come from defective hemoglobin and red blood cells in the individual. Sickle cell anemia is a commonplace name for this wide collection of symptoms and diseases. Unfortunately, the disease can be most often found in individuals of both African American and Saudi Arabian descent. This does not mean that the disease cannot be found in individuals of other cultural heritage and descent, however; after all, sickle cell disease affects over 100,000 individuals in North America alone (Know More, Do More, n.d.).

What this disease mainly affects is the production of damaged or defective red blood cells. In a healthy individual, the red blood cells are circular, with rounded edges making them appear smooth. In the individual who has sickle cell anemia, the red blood cells are shaped like sickles—leading to the name—or crescent moons. They have a 'sharp' point at the ends and are sticky in comparison to the healthy ones—this leads to the blood cells sticking to the walls of blood vessels and veins. The blood cells then continue to build up in the vessels, especially in already small vessels and lead to a slower flow of blood. Another result of these misshapen blood cells is that they get trapped in the spleen—an organ which, in turn, destroys the cells. The body then, in addition to being unable to produce healthy blood cells, is much slower at producing new ones. This leads to a generally lower amount of red blood cells in the individual's body. This will then affect the overall functioning of the body.

Therefore, generally speaking, sickle cell disease and sickle cell anemia is an autoimmune disorder, where the individual has an inability to produce healthy red blood cells.

How Is It Caused?

There is no environmental cause for sickle cell anemia. There is no way for an individual to 'catch' it from another person by being out in society together. It is not a viral or contagious illness; it is also not one that is developed or acquired over an individual's life based on their lifestyle.

Rather, sickle cell disease and anemia is a genetically inherited disease: this means that it can be passed down from parent to child. An important note here is that just because your parents have sickle cell anemia does not mean that you will also develop a full-blown case of the disease. Instead, you may simply be carrying the gene or trait which you can then pass on to your own children.

Similar to other genetically inherited diseases like cystic fibrosis, both parents must test positive for the gene for the child to have a high chance of developing the disease. If both parents have the gene, the child has just a 25% chance of being born with the disease; however, if only one parent has the disease—or simply carries the gene—then the child has a 50% chance of being a carrier as well.

With that in mind, there is no external cause for sickle cell anemia. It is actually caused by a genetic mutation in how the individual produces red blood cells that is then passed down from parent to child.

What Are the Symptoms?

The symptoms of sickle cell disease range from mild to extremely severe. For the purposes of this book, we will go over the six most common symptoms.

Anemia

Anemia is the decrease in the number and production of red blood cells in the body. This can lead to a weakness in the muscles and extreme fatigue in the individual, as their body must work harder to function. Anemia comes about in this disease because the spleen destroys the cells faster than the body can produce them, as well as the fact that sickle-shaped cells generally live about 100 days shorter than a healthy red blood cell will.

Anemia is one of the most common symptoms of sickle cell disease, therefore leading to the common interchanging of the name of the disease: sickle cell disease and sickle cell anemia. Naming the disease sickle cell anemia is not a misnomer, however, due to the fact that anemia is always a result of the production of sickle cells.

Pain

Another symptom of this autoimmune disease is for the individual to exhibit extreme amounts of pain. These episodes of pain are referred to as a crisis and is one of the most terrifying and concerning symptoms for the individual. The reasoning behind this is because the episodes of pain can last from a few hours to a number of days, and their intensity can stop daily functions and activities.

The cause of this pain is multifold. The pain can be caused by a buildup of damaged red blood cells in the vessels leading to inflammation. The pain can also be caused by organs that have been damaged due to a lack of consistent and healthy blood flow. A third reason for this pain is out of damaged nerves that can result from organ damage and poor blood flow.

Swelling of Extremities

The swelling of extremities—namely in the hands and feet—is a symptom of sickle cell anemia; this symptom can be a result from a blockage in blood flow caused by the sticky sickle-shaped cells. Swelling can also be found in other parts of the body as well, such as the abdomen or limbs.

If this is the case, the individual must seek medical intervention immediately.

Infections

Infections can occur in the individual suffering from sickle cell disease, therefore leading to frequent infections to become a symptom of the illness. Due to the fact that the sickle cells can cause organ damage, they can then affect how the body fights off infections. Organs that help fight viruses and bacteria in the body can be damaged and therefore are unable to function properly.

Furthermore, the spleen—an active agent in fighting off bacteria and strengthening the immune system of the individual—is working overtime to destroy the defective red blood cells. This leads the spleen to not function as it is originally intended to, leading to more infections in the body.

Delayed Growth

Delayed growth in the individual, specifically concerning delayed puberty in the individual, can be a symptom and result of sickle cell disease. This is because red blood cells are those that deliver oxygen throughout the body and muscles. Oxygen delivery to muscles are key to bodily growth and hormone development.

Sickle cells, as they often do not make it to organs—and are also not able to store and carry oxygen—impede on the individual's ability to circulate oxygen. This issue then affects their growth development.

Impaired Vision

Impaired vision is a symptom of sickle cell disease that is slightly controversial: poor vision can be caused by many different things. However, when it is caused by sickle cell disease, it is because the vessels leading to the eye become blocked by the moon—shaped cells. The eyes are most often affected by such blockage because they are so small and then become easily blocked.

Thus, if the individual has poor vision or sudden vision loss with no other cause, doctors will often test for sickle cell disease and sickle cell anemia.

How Is It Diagnosed?

Based on the genetic makeup and history of the individual—including their experience with the symptoms—it can be safely assumed that they are suffering from sickle cell disease and sickle cell anemia. However, an official diagnosis for sickle cell anemia is made through a minor, and generally harmless, blood test. For adults, the blood is taken from the arm; in infants and young children, the blood is usually taken from the heel of the foot. Through the blood tests, doctors are able to test the protein hemoglobin in the patient's red blood cells. Healthy blood cells carry what is referred to as hemoglobin A (Hgb A). However, individuals who have either the trait of sickle cell or the disease and anemia itself have defective hemoglobin—hemoglobin S (Hgb S)—which causes the mutation of the red blood cells from normal into sickles, or half-moons.

As with many genetically inherited diseases—or with any illnesses—early diagnosis is the key to ensuring successful treatment. Fortunately, in recent years, it is rare for an individual to be diagnosed with sickle cell anemia—or the trait, for that matter—in the later years of their life. This is because the blood test for sickle cell is included in the standard blood test for newborn. Therefore, sickle cell anemia is usually diagnosed officially within the first six months of an individual's life.

Another thing is that if there is an assumed high risk or known family trait of sickle cell disease, tests to uncover a percent chance of the disease can be done in utero—through testing the amniotic fluid in the womb. Of course, no test will be definitive until the blood is tested when the child is born.

Furthermore, the severity of the disease will not be disclosed until the child is a little older: at least 6 months old to a year.

Possible Complications

Although sickle cell anemia and sickle cell disease are not necessarily considered fatal, there can be some severe and possibly fatal complications of this disease. There can be a large buildup of red blood cells in the vessels that can block the blood flow to different areas to the body. A lack of blood flow can cause a stroke or other organs to be damaged or fail. The inconsistent blood flow can cause infection and complications internally, as the blood does not push infected cells to be destroyed. It can also cause pulmonary hypertension and other complications related to high blood pressure, as the body tries to over compensate for the poor blood flow. In some cases, it can even lead to blindness or, in males, issues with erections, as blood flow either is too high or blocked in the vessels, further putting pressure on the organs.

These complications, among others, are severe and require medical intervention as soon as possible.

Is There a Cure?

Many doctors claim that there is no cure for this disease when, in fact, that is not entirely true. In the past, some doctors and patients have had great success and supposedly been cured from this disease through a bone marrow transplant. A bone marrow transplant involves transplanting blood stem cells into the infected patient from a healthy patient, in an attempt to show the body how to strategize proper hemoglobin and red blood cells. However, this treatment is not considered to be a cure because the process of this treatment is quite complicated for the doctors and quite painful for the patient. The requirements for matching bone marrow are a lot more difficult than that of a simple blood donation. Furthermore, the marrow is taken from and given through the spine—this makes the process quite painful for both the recipient and donor. Because of this, it leads to a smaller amount of individuals being eligible or offering to be a donor. What's more is that there is a high rate of infection and rejection with this procedure which can lead to fatal complications. For example, the donor may have an undisclosed and unknown illness that is transferred along with their marrow. Of course, they go through rigorous testing before the procedure takes place; however, nothing is guaranteed. One last reason as to why a bone marrow transplant is not considered a cure for sickle cell disease and sickle cell anemia—leading to the conclusion that it is an incurable disease—is that such a procedure does not always work. The injection of new red blood cells is with the intention that they will 'show' the defective red blood cells how to function properly. However, depending on the severity of the individual's sickle cell anemia, the healthy red blood cells given through the stem cells and marrow may be overpowered by the body's defective cells. In this case, many patients will in fact feel better for a short while then revert back to their symptoms over time.

For this reason, it is considered that there is no cure for sickle cell disease or sickle cell anemia. That is why common practice and treatment is focused on coping with the symptoms. This is also why an early diagnosis is preferred to begin the coping process as early as possible.

However, just because there is no cure does not mean that living with sickle cell anemia has to be discouraging. This book will help you open your eyes to the possible ways of coping and thriving with the disease.

Myths Surrounding Sickle Cell Disease

One way of coping with sickle cell disease and sickle cell anemia is to be educated about the illness, who it affects, and the specifics. Therefore, this section is meant to educate the sickle cell disease sufferer—or the individual who is close to a sufferer—more about their disease by explaining away and exploring some myths and common questions surrounding the illness.

Myth 1: Only people of African descent can have sickle cell disease.

False. Indeed, there have been studies to show that individuals of African descent and heritage show a higher number of cases. However, this does not mean that individuals of other cultures and ancestry are not also affected. Sickle cell diseases affect millions of individuals worldwide, with over 300,000 babies being born and diagnosed with a form of sickle cell disease or sickle cell anemia every year.

Myth 2: Sickle cell diseases and sickle cell anemia are contagious diseases.

False. Sickle cell disease and sickle cell anemia are inherited by the child from their parents in their fetal development.

Myth 3: Sickle cell diseases are not serious and are short-term conditions.

False. All sickle cell diseases and sickle cell anemia are long-term and lifelong illnesses that can have a detrimental effect on the life of the individual. What's more is that when the disease is not treated or successfully coped with, it can lead to severe medical consequences. These consequences can range from severe depression and mental stress, to blood clots, stroke, or even death.

Myth 4: It is only the defective moon-shaped or sickle-shaped cells that cause pain for the individual.

False. Pain and the pain crisis in sickle cell diseases can be caused by an buildup of stuck cells in addition to lack of oxygen in muscles and organs, organ damage, and joint pain coming from weak connective tissue.

Myth 5: People with sickle cell disease seek out pain medicine even though they may not need it.

False. Sickle cell pain is quite severe, intense, and debilitating. More often than not, over-the-counter pain relievers do not work; therefore, doctors will prescribe heavier and stronger pain medicine. Also, many sufferers of sickle cell diseases opt to not take pain relievers, as the side effects cause more harm. What's more is that the pain crisis of sickle cell disease is often a sign that there is a worse complication, so many will then seek medical intervention.

Myth 6: People with sickle cell disease are unmotivated and lack initiative.

False. Individuals who suffer from a sickle cell disease and sickle cell anemia are not necessarily unmotivated on principle. Sickle cell diseases and sickle cell anemia have a great effect on the body of the individual in addition to the mind. Depression can be developed due to chronic pain and feeling as though they cannot have a 'regular' life. Furthermore, sickle cell diseases and sickle cell anemia can dictate careers and day-to-day function of the individual, as they physically may not be able to do certain tasks.

Myth 7: Sufferers of sickle cell disease can lead a normal life.

True. With proper coping methods and treatment, an individual diagnosed with a sickle cell disease or sickle cell anemia can lead a relatively normal life in comparison to others who do not have the illness. Although some jobs and sports may not be suggested for the individual, ultimately there is no reason for an individual who has been diagnosed with a sickle cell disease and sickle cell anemia to miss out on any life experience.

Myth 8: Treatments for sickle cell diseases are the same for everyone.

False. The treatments for sickle cell symptoms are different for each individual, as they are geared toward the individual's specific types of disease and symptoms. Furthermore, treatments for the individual change of time while the individual grows. This is because symptoms will change as the body develops. Therefore, not only are sickle cell diseases and sickle cell anemia lifelong battles, the development of the treatments and coping methods are a lifelong journey as well.

Coping With Sickle Cell Anemia

Generally speaking, the way to cope with sickle cell diseases and sickle cell anemia is to stay positive, take care of mental health, and treat the symptoms preventively as they surface.

However, this topic has been divided into three sections for the individual to reference to help ensure symptoms are being treated and mental health is taken care of. These sections are: Daily Coping Methods, General Coping Strategies, and Occasional Coping Needs.

Daily Coping Methods

Daily coping methods for the symptoms of a sickle cell disease and sickle cell anemia are those that should be performed daily or a semi-regular basis in order for the sufferer to reap the benefits. These daily actions and methods are small enough for the individual to do every day, as to not be discouraged to continue and for them to be successful. They also do not take up much time for the individual, leaving them time and opportunity to have a normal life.

Drink eight to 12 8-oz glasses of water per day

Drinking enough water during the day, every day, is an important health strategy for any individual. However, it is especially important for those suffering from a sickle cell disease. This is because water helps to keep the muscles and organs hydrated and functioning properly. In addition, water can help to ensure oxygen is being delivered throughout the body. Dehydration for the individual suffering from a sickle cell disease and sickle cell anemia can be dangerous, as dehydration constricts the blood vessels and cramps the muscles. For an individual whose blood vessels may already be obstructed with a buildup of blood cells, dehydration can be extremely detrimental, as it can bring about a pain crisis or other severe complications such as swelling.

Exercise

The individual suffering from a sickle cell disease should aim to complete 15 minutes of light exercise per day. Just as exercise is important for every individual, it is increasingly important for the individual suffering from sickle cell disease and sickle cell anemia. This is because exercise can encourage blood circulation throughout the body. Light movement and exercise encourages muscles to flex and stretch which helps them, in turn, bring in oxygen. Exercise can also encourage an increase in water intake, as the individual may experience thirst after working out.

Meditate

Another daily coping method to help the individual who is suffering from a sickle cell disease and sickle cell anemia is daily meditation. There is so much stress and mental anguish that happens with consistently worrying about pain and symptoms. In turn, this stress can manifest itself within the body by, for example, triggering a pain crisis. Therefore, it is suggested that the individual should try participating in a daily meditation session. Even meditating for up to 10 minutes a day can help to bring down blood pressure and stress levels within the individual. A further exploration of keeping a clear and positive mind, in addition to the guided steps of how to meditate, will be presented in the first help guide that follows.

Journal

The last daily coping method that can help an individual who is suffering from a sickle cell disease is to keep a journal and provide a daily entry. Journaling every day can help individuals track their symptoms in addition to tracking symptom triggers. Keeping up-to-date records of what helps and what worsens specific symptoms can help the individual, their doctors and specialists, and even family members. It can help better understand what the individual needs to be successful. Journaling can also help keep track of water intake, exercise, and mental stability. Depending on the needs of the individual and sufferer, a journal can also include positive affirmations—as well as meditative mantras that can help to improve lessen the mental stress of the individual.

General Coping Strategies

General Coping Strategies are those suggestions made to the individual who is suffering from a sickle cell disease and sickle cell anemia that have extended benefits. Unlike the daily coping methods, these strategies do not yield results or effects right away. They are long-term goals the individual should consider to maintain to ensure proper health and submission of sickle cell symptoms.

Do Not Smoke

Due to the chemicals found in cigarettes, smoking can constrict the individual's blood vessels. Again, constriction of blood vessels can be dangerous for any individual, however—for the individual who is suffering from potentially already obstructed blood vessels—further constriction can have detrimental effects. Therefore, any person suffering from a sickle cell disease and sickle cell anemia should not smoke. In addition, smoking can cause other diseases and illnesses that can be worsened by the symptoms of sickle cell disease and sickle cell anemia.

Develop Good Hygiene

Developing and maintaining a good hygiene routine can help the individual who is suffering from sickle cell disease and sickle cell anemia, as it can lessen the chance of lowering an already compromised immune system and decreasing the chance of contracting an infection.

Stay Up-To-Date With Vaccines

Along the same line of reasoning for developing a good hygiene routine, the individual should also stay up to date with their vaccines and immunizations. By staying up to date with vaccines, the individual can lessen the chance of contracting a virus or infection, which can have dangerous consequences on an already weakened immune system.

Go To Therapy

Another general suggestion for coping with the challenges and symptoms of sickle cell disease is for the individual to attend therapy. This does not need to happen once a week and it does not need to happen on a regular basis. Instead, it is suggested for the individual to find a therapist for them to talk to if the need arises. As stated previously, sickle cell diseases can have an immense strain on the mental stability of the individual. Therefore, going to therapy to discuss the mental stress and feelings can help maintain a positive outlook in spite of their diagnosis.

Dress Appropriately

Extreme weather temperatures—such as extreme heat or extreme cold—can make life much more difficult for the individual suffering from sickle cell disease and sickle cell anemia. Therefore, it is a good idea that the individual generally put effort into dressing appropriately for the weather: both indoors and outdoors. By doing so, individuals can avoid—or lessen the chances and severity of—having a pain crisis or the surfacing of other symptoms and complications associated with the disease.

Stay Away From Decongestants

Interestingly, individuals who suffer from sickle cell disease and sickle cell anemia should avoid the use of decongestants. This is because, in order for the decongestant to work, they constrict certain blood vessels and affect blood flow to certain areas of the body. Referring back to the suggestion of not smoking and staying hydrated, further constriction of blood vessels can have detrimental effects on the individual.

Watch Your Diet

For the individual who has sickle cell disease and sickle cell anemia, their diet plays an important role. There are suggestions that these individuals eat a balanced diet that is not high in fat, salt, or sugar. This is because fat, salt, and sugar can affect the consistency and flow of blood in addition to the delivery of oxygen to the muscles and organs. Therefore, individuals suffering from sickle cell disease and sickle cell anemia should eat a balanced diet full of fruits, vegetables, and whole grains.

Plan and Prep For Vacations Accordingly

Another general coping mechanism and strategy for those individuals who suffer from sickle cell disease and sickle cell anemia—especially for those who have a frequent pain crisis—pay attention to their vacations. Vacation activities such as plane travel, swimming in the ocean, and scuba diving can have negative effects on the individual. This is because the pressurized aircraft, the inconsistent temperature of the ocean water, and pressure changes when scuba diving can affect blood flow of oxygen delivery in the individual. Therefore, a doctor should be consulted when vacations, specifically tropical vacations, are being planned or considered.

Occasional Coping Interventions

Even with a strict adherence to the daily coping methods and general strategies, the sufferer of a sickle cell disease and sickle cell anemia may still experience an occasional flare up of symptoms, like a pain crisis or extreme fatigue. Therefore, there are intervention strategies that can be used occasionally in order to help subdue a symptom. These occasional coping interventions can also be used if the individual is not successful in their daily and general coping methods and is thus experiencing symptoms.

Intravenous Fluids

Intravenous fluids are given if the individual is extremely dehydrated. This is an occasional and emergent coping intervention. Although it is usually successful, it is not one that is preferred among medical professionals and patients.

Supplemental Oxygen

Supplemental oxygen is often given during a pain crisis or other complications and is normally administered through a mask.

Blood Transfusion

A blood transfusion is another option for an occasional coping intervention. However, it is often not used regularly as it requires much preparation, a matching donor, and increases the chance of infection.

Prescription and Over-the-Counter Medications

Over-the-counter pain-relieving medication can be used on occasion, or regularly, for the individual during a pain crisis. However, its use should be followed by a consultation with the doctor to ensure the proper over-the-counter medication is being used. Stronger pain-relieving medications, such as narcotics, may be prescribed if over-the-counter medications do not provide enough relief. However, narcotics pose the risk of addiction in addition to other medical problems if not taken properly or too often.

These occasional interventions should only be used once in a while and should not be the individual's primary coping methods, as they can have a harder effect on the body and make their disease worse overall. It is highly suggested that the individual develop and comply with the daily and general coping strategies to avoid the possible and dangerous complications of the occasional interventions.

Chapter Five: Other Types of Anemia

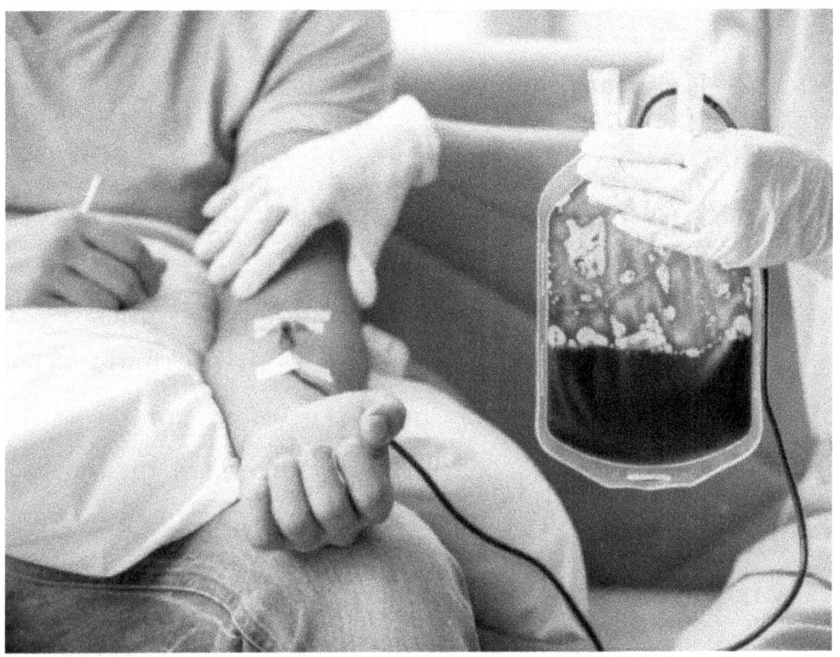

Microcytic Anemia

Microcytic anemia is one of several types of anemia characterized by small red blood cells. Aside from being small, the red blood cells are characteristically hypochromic – meaning that they are paler than they should be. Due to both of these facts, this condition is commonly referred to as microcytic hypochromic anemia. In this chapter, you will learn the basics about this particular type of anemia including its cause, symptoms and treatment options.

Basics of the Condition

Microcytic anemia is a type of blood disorder characterized by abnormally small red blood cells. There are several possible reasons that the blood cells might be too small including improper hemoglobin synthesis or insufficient production of hemoglobin in the body. This condition is very common and it is often compared to macrocytic anemia – a condition characterized by the red blood cells being larger than normal.

Cases of microcytic anemia are typically diagnosed based on mean cell volume (MCV) tests. If tests reveal an MCV level less than 80 – meaning the diameter of your red blood cells measures less than 80 microns in diameter – it could be an indication of microcytic anemia. In many cases, this type of anemia is synonymous with iron-deficiency anemia, mainly due to the fact that the most common cause of microcytic anemia is iron deficiency.

Unfortunately, the symptoms of microcytic anemia are easy to miss and are commonly confused with the symptoms of other conditions. This being the case, many people do not realize they have the disease until they go to the doctor for a regular checkup. The symptoms of microcytic anemia include fatigue, shortness of breath, pale skin and decrease in stamina. If you are experiencing any of these symptoms, you may want to consult your doctor to have your blood tested for anemia.

Other symptoms of microcytic anemia include:

- Decrease in appetite
- Unexplained weight loss
- Severe headaches
- Changes in nail texture
- Chest pain
- Rapid heartbeat
- Paleness in the skin and gums
- Strange food cravings

Cause and Effect

The causes of microcytic anemia vary and may include poor diet, unhealthy lifestyle choices or a variety of underlying conditions. The most common causes are:

- Iron-deficient diet
- Internal bleeding
- Chronic disease
- Lead poisoning

Your body requires a minimum of 1 mg of iron every day in order to maintain healthy function. Most nutritionists, however, recommend a daily intake around 8 to 10 mg per day. The best way to meet your daily recommendation for iron is to eat plenty of iron-rich foods like leafy greens, red meat and legumes. If these foods are missing from your diet you could end up with an iron deficiency which could contribute to microcytic anemia.

Another common cause of microcytic anemia is excessive blood loss. This blood loss may be due to heavy menstruation in women of child-bearing age but it is also commonly due to internal bleeding in the gastrointestinal tract. Unfortunately, internal bleeding can be hard to diagnose because it is easy to miss in the stool. If your doctor suspects microcytic anemia, you may be asked to submit a stool sample for analysis.

Certain chronic diseases may cause the iron levels in your body to decline which could cause or contribute to microcytic anemia. Severe infections and inflammation may also have this effect. When your body is battling chronic disease, it could result in your red blood cells having a shorter lifespan – it may also affect your body's ability to produce new red blood cells. In cases like this, normocytic anemia is common but it can easily progress to microcytic anemia.

The final cause of microcytic anemia, lead poisoning, is less common than the others but it is no less serious. Lead poisoning typically takes months or years to develop and it most commonly occurs with exposure to lead-based paint or lead-contaminated dust.

Children under the age of 6 are especially vulnerable to lead poisoning and it can have devastating effects on their growth and mental development.

Treatment Options

In order to confirm a diagnosis and to treat microcytic anemia, your doctor will need to perform a series of tests. These tests are designed to rule out or identify any underlying conditions which could be causing or contributing to your microcytic anemia.

The goal of any treatment for anemia is to increase the ability of your red blood cells to carry oxygen. In the case of microcytic anemia, treatments are designed to increase the MVC of your red blood cells to make this possible.

The main cause of microcytic anemia – iron deficiency – can easily be treated with iron supplementation or by simply increasing the number of iron-rich foods you consume on a regular basis.

If an increase in dietary iron doesn't work, your doctor may attempt other forms of medical treatment – in some cases, this may involve medication.

Pernicious Anemia

Pernicious anemia is a type of anemia that involves vitamin B12. The term pernicious was used for this type of anemia because of the lack of treatment available many years ago which made its inevitably fatal. Fortunately, modern science has found a cure for this condition.

Pernicious anemia can affect every race, but studies show that a fair-haired people are more susceptible to this condition. Pernicious anemia usually doesn't show up before the age of 30, although there are some rare cases where it developed in children.

The body needs vitamin B12 and folate to create red blood cells. It is also needed in the creation of DNA and in nerve functioning. Vitamin B12 can be found in food produced from animals such as meat, poultry, dairy and eggs. Breads and cereals can also contain vitamin B12.

Pernicious anemia happens when the body cannot create enough red blood cells due to the inability to absorb vitamin B12. The body cannot absorb vitamin B12 because of different intrinsic factors such as the lack of protein in the stomach. Problems in the small intestine can also prevent the absorption of vitamin B12. Poor diet can also cause folate and vitamin B12 deficiency. Without enough vitamin B12, the red blood cells are usually too large because it does not divide equally. This can make it difficult to release the red blood cells from the bone marrow and enter the blood stream.

Who is susceptible to pernicious anemia?

People who are susceptible to the disease include those who cannot absorb enough vitamin B12, lack intrinsic factor and do not acquire enough vitamin B12 through their food.

- **People who lack intrinsic factors**

Intrinsic factors deliver vitamin B12 into the intestines where it is absorbed. Autoimmune response can also affect the ability of the body to produce intrinsic factors. Other disease such as type 1 Diabetes and Addison's disease. It can also cause autoimmune response. Surgery that removes a part of the stomach can also cause a decrease in intrinsic factors. This is due to the removal of the part of the body that creates a protein during surgery.

- **People who cannot absorb vitamin B12**

People cannot absorb vitamin B12 if there is too much bacteria in the intestine. Bacteria can block the walls of the intestine and make it difficult for the body to absorb vitamin B12. The bacteria also consume the vitamin B12 even before it is used by the body. This is the most common cause of pernicious anemia in older people. Gastrointestinal infection and disorder can also affect the absorption of vitamin B12. Medication can also alter bacterial growth in the body and prevent proper nutrient absorption.

- **People who do not get enough vitamin B12 in their diet**

Vitamin B12 can be found in food that come from animals and various dietary supplements. Older people who suffer from alcoholism can also be at risk of pernicious anemia if they do not take enough vitamin B12 in their diet.

Signs And Symptoms Of Pernicious Anemia

The body stores sufficient vitamin B12 that can last for about 3 to 5 years. As soon as the body has exhausted its supply of vitamin B12, the signs and symptoms of pernicious anemia begins to appear.

Some symptoms are caused by vitamin B12 deficiency while others are the result of vitamin B12 deficiency causes. The most typical symptom of anemia is tiredness. The body does not have adequate blood that can transport oxygen in the body. Anemia can also cause rapid heartbeat, dizziness, and palpitations.

Here are some of the signs and symptoms of pernicious anemia:

- Cold feet and hands
- Pale skin and yellowish skin
- Bleeding gums and nail beds
- Chest pain
- Heart failure
- Sore tongue
- Poor appetite
- Disturbed balance

When left untreated, pernicious anemia can also lead to sensory and nerve damage that has neurological effects. This type of anemia can also affect the gastrointestinal system and cardiovascular systems of the body that can affect a person's senses and tendon reflexes. Paranoia and delirium may also occur. Gastric polyps can also develop which can even lead to gastric cancer. Vitamin B12 deficiency can also affect the cells on the cervix, which can result to a false positive pap result.

Pernicious anemia can progress over time and if left untreated. It can eventually lead to death after years of suffering. However, replacement therapy, medication and lifestyle changes can allow the patient to live a normal life.

Hemolytic Anemia

Hemolytic anemia is characterized by the abnormal breakdown of red blood cells either in the blood vessels themselves or elsewhere in the body. The causes for this particular form of anemia vary, as does the severity of it. In this section, you will learn the basics about this form of anemia including its cause, symptoms and treatment options.

Basics of the Condition

The marrow in your bones is responsible for producing new red blood cells – it also produces white blood cells and platelets. As your red blood cells die, your bone marrow produces new ones so your body stays in balance. In the case of hemolytic anemia, however, your red blood cells die faster than your bone marrow is able to produce them. The term for the death or destruction of red blood cells is "hemolysis," which is where this condition gets its name.

There are two main forms of hemolytic anemia – intrinsic and extrinsic. Intrinsic hemolytic anemia occurs when the red blood cells in the body are defective. This condition is typically genetically inherited, often in people that are suffering from sickle cell anemia or thalassemia.

Extrinsic anemia, on the other hand, occurs when the spleen destroys healthy blood cells. Normally, the spleen is responsible for disposing of old red blood cells but it may malfunction and begin to destroy healthy cells in the case of hemolytic anemia. Healthy blood cell destruction may also be the result of autoimmune disorders, leukemia or lymphoma.

Hemolytic anemia can affect individuals of any age. According to the National Heart, Lung and Blood Institute, however, it is more common in African Americans then in Caucasians. This may be due to the fact that sickle cell anemia is more common in African Americans.

If you are experiencing symptoms of anemia, your doctor may perform a detailed medical history as well as a physical exam. During this exam, your doctor may ask you to lie flat so he can examine your abdomen.

Tenderness or swelling in the abdomen during a physical exam may indicate hemolytic anemia. This suspicion may be confirmed through blood tests and, in some cases, a bone marrow aspiration or biopsy may be required.

Cause and Effect

The overarching cause of hemolytic anemia is the destruction of red blood cells.

There are many different possible causes for this destruction, however. Some of these causes may include:

- Typhoid fever
- Epstein-Barr virus
- Sickle cell anemia
- Hepatitis
- Streptococcus
- Leukemia
- Lymphoma
- Side effects of medication
- Lupus
- Blood disorders
- Exposure to toxins
- Other infections

In some cases, hemolytic anemia has no identifiable cause. When this happens, you may have to go through various tests to rule out underlying conditions and you might have to try different treatments until something works.

a.) Autoimmune Hemolytic Anemia

Also known as AIHA, autoimmune hemolytic anemia occurs when your immune system produces antibodies that attack healthy red blood cells. It isn't known why this happens, but it can be very dangerous. Autoimmune hemolytic anemia accounts for about half of all cases of hemolytic anemia and it is often marked by rapid onset. Though the exact cause is unknown, having certain infections or diseases can increase your risk for this type of anemia. Some of these diseases include:

- Autoimmune disease (ex: lupus)
- Epstein-Barr virus
- Chronic lymphocytic leukemia
- Non-Hodgkin's lymphoma
- Blood cancers
- Hepatitis or HIV
- Cytomegalovirus
- Mycoplasma pneumonia
-

In some cases, autoimmune hemolytic anemia develops after an individual undergoes a blood and marrow stem cell transplant. Some cases of AIHA are more active at certain temperatures. In cases where the body produces warm antibodies, the antibodies are most active in warm temperature (ex: body temperature).

Other types of AIHA are cold-reactive, in which case the antibodies are more active at cold temperatures. Cases like this may be exacerbated when the extremities (ex: hands and feet) are exposed to temperatures below 50°F.

Treatment Options

The treatment of hemolytic anemia varies depending on the cause of the condition.

Your age, health and tolerance for certain medications may also play a role in determining your treatment options. The populat treatment options for this condition include:

- Blood transfusion
- Intravenous immune globulin
- Corticosteroid medications
- Surgery

Blood Transfusion:

A blood transfusion is the quickest way to treat hemolytic anemia. A transfusion may be given to quickly increase your red blood cell count to replace those cells that have been destroyed. Even with a blood transfusion, however, further treatment may be required to remedy the underlying cause of red blood cell destruction.

Intravenous Immune Globulin:

Low red blood cell count can have a negative impact on your immune system –e specially if your hemolytic anemia is concurrent with an autoimmune disorder. In cases like this, you may be treated with intravenous immune globulin to boost your immune system function.

Corticosteroid Medications:

Medication with corticosteroids is another common treatment for hemolytic anemia that originates from autoimmune disease. The corticosteroids will help to stop your body from producing the antibodies that destroy healthy red blood cells.

Surgery:

In most cases, surgery is considered to be a last resort. This treatment may be necessary if your spleen is to blame for the destruction of healthy red blood cells and if it can't be remedied in any other way.

Normocytic Anemia

Normocytic anemia is most commonly seen in individuals over 85 years of age. The risk for this condition increases with age, affecting more than 40% of men over the age of 85. Due to its prevalence, normocytic anemia is the most common type of anemia. In this section, you will learn the basics about this form of anemia including its cause, symptoms and treatment options.

Basics of the Condition

Whereas some types of anemia are characterized by having blood cells of abnormal size, normocytic anemia involves a reduced number of normal-sized red blood cells. This condition may be characterized by any of the following:

- Decreased production of normal RBCS or red blood cells
- Increased loss or destruction of RBCS or red blood cells
- Uncompensated increase in plasma volume
- Mixture of conditions resulting in microcytic and macrocytic anemia

It is important to realize that nearly all cases of anemia begin as normocytic (decreased number of normal-sized blood cells). As the causes of this condition progress and develop, normocytic anemia may develop into another form of anemia.

Normocytic anemia is, however, the most common type of anemia and it is most commonly seen in older individuals over 85 years of age.

The symptoms of normocytic anemia are easy to miss because they tend to develop slowly over time. In many cases, your doctor will only test for the condition if you experience a sudden increase in the severity of symptoms – this may be an indication of an underlying disease. Once a case of normocytic anemia has fully progressed, some of the common symptoms include:

- Weakness or dizziness
- Pallor as a result of lack of blood flow
- Getting tired very easily

You may experience other symptoms as well, depending on the underlying cause of your normocytic anemia. Your treatment options will vary depending on these conditions as well.

Cause and Effect

Though normocytic anemia is most common among older individuals, age is not the sole factor – this condition is something an individual can be born with as well. Normocytic anemia is a condition which often occurs in the presence of or as a result of another health condition. Some of these underlying conditions often include:

- Kidney disease
- Rheumatoid arthritis
- Thyroid problems
- Certain cancers
- Chronic infection
- Inflammatory diseases
- Marrow failure

Chronic Diseases:

The most common type of normocytic anemia is that which is associated with chronic disease – it is also the second most common form of anemia in the world (iron-deficiency anemia being the first). Normocytic anemia has been linked to a number of chronic diseases including inflammatory conditions, severe infections, neoplasms and systemic diseases.

Cases of normocytic anemia related to renal or endocrine problems are generally not classified as an anemia of chronic disease. Some of the hallmark signs of anemia related to chronic disease include decreased serum iron levels, decreased transferrin levels and normal or increased ferritin levels. All three of these conditions result in making iron inaccessible to the body, though it may actually be present.

Endocrine Deficiency:

Some of the most common states of endocrine deficiency include adrenal insufficiency, pituitary insufficiency, hypothyroidism and hypogonadism. These conditions may also result in bone marrow failure due to reduced erythropoietin secretion.

Renal Failure:

Anemia is very common in cases of both acute and chronic renal failure (kidney failure). In most cases, it is normocytic anemia but it can progress to microcytic anemia. Anemia typically occurs during renal failure because uremic metabolites in the body reduce the lifespan of the red blood cells in circulation. Tests for this type of normocytic anemia can be difficult to decipher because the results often do not correlate to test results seen in other types of anemia.

Other Causes:

Though uncommon, normocytic anemia may be caused by bone marrow infiltration or failure. The diagnosis for this type of anemia typically involves a bone marrow biopsy.

Treatment Options

The treatment for normocytic anemia is generally the treatment for the underlying condition. This being the case, the first step in treatment of normocytic anemia is to identify the cause of the condition.

In order to diagnose the underlying condition, your doctor may perform various blood tests – in some cases you may even have to go through a bone marrow biopsy.

In cases of severe normocytic anemia, your doctor may recommend treatment with erythropoietin. Erythropoietin is a type of glycoprotein hormone which controls red blood cell production in the body. This treatment is especially common in cases of anemia related to renal disease or failure – it has also been shown to be effective in cases of anemia of chronic disease.

Chapter Six: Anemia in Pregnancy

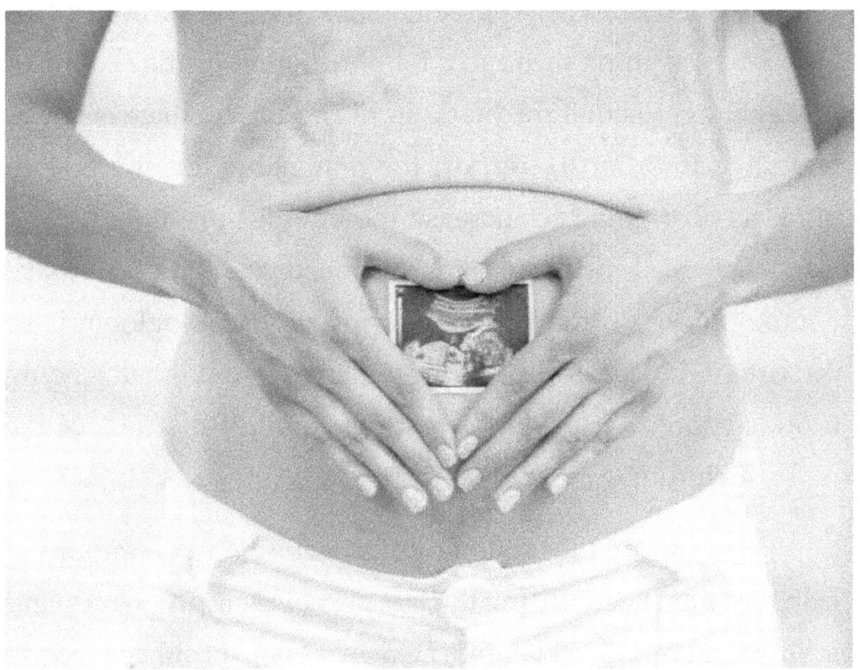

Understand Anemia in Pregnancy

Being pregnant is a wonderful period in a woman's life. It is the time where you are creating a new living being, within yourself, someone who is going to rely on you for the long term and who is going to have you wrapped around their finger in no time. But even with all of the wonders of pregnancy and birth, there are still a few issues that can occur. One of these issues is anemia in pregnancy.

When you are pregnant, you are going to notice that your body is going through a lot of different changes. One of these changes is that the blood in the body will increase by at least 20% in order to support the new baby; this increase in blood is also going to increase the amount of vitamins and iron that the body is going to need in order to make hemoglobin. You may be wondering why hemoglobin is so important. It is basically the protein in the blood that is going to make sure that oxygen is getting to all of the cells of the body, including your baby.

It is normal for women to be lacking in the amount of iron that they need during the last part of their pregnancy and a bit of anemia is to be expected in most. Problems arise when this iron deficiency becomes worse and the woman becomes anemic. Anemia that is severe can often put the baby at risk because they are not getting the nutrients and oxygen that they need to survive. It also is going to put a further burden on the mother during labor because it makes it more likely that she will lose more blood than she would have otherwise.

There are some risks that can occur with anemia when it becomes severe or it is not taken care of. Since it is so easy to take care of and to catch, most women do not have to worry about this, but those who are not tested or do not follow the doctor's advice may find that the anemia will result in some issues for them, such as postpartum depression and issues with bleeding after pregnancy, and for their baby, such as anemia at birth and some forms of birth defects.

It is important to take the right precautions to know if you are at risk of developing anemia and what you can do to stop it.

Some ways to tell if you are at a higher risk for this disorder include the following:

- Having two pregnancies that were close together;
- You are carrying more than one child in the same pregnancy;
- Have severe morning sickness, which includes a lot of vomiting;
- Are not taking in enough iron (this issue can often be fixed with a prenatal vitamin and a good diet); and
- Had a menstrual flow before getting pregnant that was really heavy.

Of course, those who are not in any of these groups can get anemia, as well. Your doctor is going to perform routine blood tests throughout the pregnancy to determine if iron levels are high enough in your blood. They will also recommend eating a good diet and taking a prenatal vitamin from the beginning of the pregnancy to avoid any complications that can arise from anemia

Many women wonder if it is possible to prevent anemia. While more of the treatments will be discussed below, it is completely possible to be able to prevent anemia if the right steps are taken.

It is usually recommended that you start out with a good diet right from when you hear about being pregnant, if not before. You also need to make sure that you are taking in enough iron to help your body out. Talk to your doctor about anemia and determine together if you may be at risk for developing it in your pregnancy. Tests can be done to determine whether or not anemia is present and what you will be able to do to help it from getting worse.

The best thing that you can do in order to deal with any anemia that you may be dealing with is to get it found early. The earlier that you are able to find out about the anemia, the easier it is to treat and the less damage that is going to occur. If your doctor does not already do this right at the beginning of the pregnancy or early on, make sure that you request that they do a blood test to check your iron and hemoglobin levels. You may also want to request to get the test done a few times throughout the pregnancy; just because the anemia is not present right from the beginning does not mean that it will not show up later on as more strain is put on your body while the baby continues to grow.

Causes

When you are pregnant, it is more likely that you are going to deal with anemia compared to other points in your life. This is because you are producing more blood to keep up with the demand of the baby as well as your own needs. All of this extra work makes it harder to get the iron that your body needs. Having a mild case of anemia is considered normal during a pregnancy, however, the issues come when you get a more severe form of anemia and are not getting the oxygen that is needed to keep yourself and your baby healthy.

There are several different causes of having anemia and the one you are dealing with is going to depend on the nutrients that you are missing in your blood. Some of these will be discussed below.

Iron Deficiency

The first type of anemia that you can have is iron deficiency. This is the type where you are not giving your body the iron that it needs in order to stay healthy and produce hemoglobin. Hemoglobin is very important in your blood because it is the protein that is present in the blood that is able to carry oxygen through the body from the lungs. Basically, without iron, you are not creating the hemoglobin you need and then, you are not getting the oxygen to your body parts like it is supposed to.

This is the most common anemia that you will suffer from when you are dealing with anemia in pregnancy. Often the best way to take care of this nutrient deficiency is with eating a proper diet. If you are getting in enough fruits and vegetables and lean meats to the diet, it is not as likely that you will become low on iron. Most doctors will also recommend that you take a prenatal vitamin that has some extra iron in it to ensure that issues do not come up.

When you are tested for anemia, it is most likely that the doctor is going to test first to see if you are low on iron. This is the most common form of anemia and often the easiest to correct at an early stage to getting the right tests and taking in the right amount of nutrition from diet and prenatal pills can be the best way to prevent this form of anemia.

Folate Deficiency

Iron deficiency is not the only problem that you may experience when it comes to anemia. It is also possible that your body is low on folate or folic acid. This is a type of vitamin B that is important in helping the body create enough red blood cells that can carry the oxygen and other nutrients to the rest of the body.

Throughout the pregnancy, a woman will need to make sure that she is getting the folate that her body needs to make new cells. Sometimes, it is difficult to get this particular nutrient into the diet with eating healthy foods. While it is possible, it is a bit more difficult than taking in iron. Without the right amount of folate in the body, there can even be birth defects so taking in enough is critical if you would like to have a healthy pregnancy.

This is the vitamin that is the most difficult to get a hold of during pregnancy. It is needed in much higher demand while you are pregnant compared to other times in your life and getting it out of food is a little more of a challenge compared to iron or other nutrients. This is why starting a prenatal vitamin early on is so important. It gives you the important folic acid that your body needs in order to stay happy and healthy, as well as keep your baby healthy while in gestation.

One of the best ways to get folate into the body is to take a prenatal vitamin. Most of the major ones you will be able to find come with the folate that you need in order to have a healthy pregnancy. Make sure to eat a balanced diet and take a prenatal throughout your pregnancy to make sure you are getting enough of this important nutrient.

Vitamin B12 Deficiency

In addition to folic acid and iron, the body is going to need some vitamin B12 during pregnancy in order to stay healthy because it is critical in forming red blood cells that are healthy. If the woman is not able to get in enough of this vitamin, her body is going to have some difficulties producing the blood cells that are needed. It is possible to get this vitamin from the foods that you eat, such as, eggs, dairy products, poultry, and meat, but vegetarians and vegans will find this hard to do.

Anyone is able to get this deficiency if they are not eating the foods that they are supposed to. Make sure that you are taking care of your body with plenty of good food and a prenatal vitamin if needed to avoid the issues that can come from this form of anemia.

Signs or Symptoms

It is important that you know the signs and symptoms of having anemia during your pregnancy in order to get it taken care of right away. The earlier that you start to take care of the anemia, the less likely it is to cause any issues for you or the baby. Anemia can happen even if you are taking the right precautions and eating a good diet, so it is still important for you to know the signs.

There are a few signs that you should look for in order to determine if you are suffering from anemia or not. These would include:

- Pale nails, lips, and skin—this is due to oxygen and other nutrients not being able to get to your skin and nails with the loss of iron and folate.
- Feeling weak and tired—yes, it is normal to feel worn out when you are pregnant and that is something that all pregnant women are going to feel. But if you seem to be more tired than what is considered normal and you have trouble finding any motivation or being able to get out of bed, it could possibly be anemia. Discuss any excess tiredness with your doctor to figure out if this could be the cause or not.
- Dizziness—this is another symptom that could be a sign of anemia, but which could also be a sign of anemia. If you are dizzy when getting up, sitting down, or doing your normal activities it could be a sign of anemia. This issue will occur when the brain is not getting the amount of oxygen that it needs in order to function properly because not enough iron is in the blood.
- Short breath—you may experience the need to breathe faster or heavier because you are trying to make up for the lack of oxygen carrying cells in the blood.

- Rapid heartbeat—due to your shortness of breath, the heart may start to pump faster. This will result in the blood moving through the body faster than before and trying to get more nutrients to the body. You may also experience the need to breathe more heavily when this occurs.
- Trouble with concentration—this is similar to the dizziness issue in the fact that you are going to not be giving the brain the oxygen that it needs. This means that your brain is not going to be able to concentrate on the things that are important to you. If you are having more issues than normal with concentration, you may need to be tested for anemia.

As you can see, there are a lot of symptoms that are present for anemia but which can also be normal things that you will see when you are pregnant. This is one of the reasons why it is so difficult for some women to realize that they may be suffering from something that is worse than normal pregnancy symptoms. Many doctors will order routine tests to check hemoglobin levels, as well as, iron levels to determine if anemia is present.

Test to Check for Anemia

If you are suffering from severe forms of the symptoms that are listed above, it may be a good idea for you to check out if you have anemia. Discuss these symptoms with your doctor and they can choose which form of anemia test they would like to have done. In some cases, your doctor may already have plans to run tests throughout the pregnancy to ensure that anemia does not show up and if it does you are able to take care of it early before worse problems occur.

There are a few tests that you will be able to get in order to test for anemia. The first one is the hemoglobin test. In this test, the doctor is going to take some blood and measure how much hemoglobin is present in the blood. This is the protein that is critical to helping you carry the all-important oxygen to your body. If it is low on the test, you will have anemia and need to start taking in more iron to your body to prevent any other issues.

Another test that can be done is known as the Hematocrit Test. This is going to check for other forms of anemia by checking how many red blood cells you have as a percentage of the whole blood. You will just need a small sample of blood to test this one out.

Often your doctor may test for both in one sample of blood to save time and to make sure that no anemia is present in the body regardless of the form. Remember above that there is more than one issue that can come with anemia and these two tests can effectively check for both kinds. Getting these tests done at least once during your pregnancy can be really critical to keeping you and your baby healthy throughout the pregnancy.

Effects

Many pregnant women do not understand the bad effects which can occur if they have anemia. They think that they can just ignore the tired feelings and that they will have a normal pregnancy even without the right nutrients. Having this thought process is going to make things very difficult for them because having anemia during pregnancy can make a lot of issues occur. This section will look at some of the negative effects that can happen if you start to develop severe anemia and do not get it treated in time.

Some of the effects that occur with severe as well as untreated anemia include:

- A baby who is born early or who has a low birth weight—since your baby is not getting the oxygen and other nutrients they need through the blood, they are not going to be able to grow and thrive like they should.

- Blood transfusions—without the proper iron and other nutrients in the body, it becomes hard for the blood to stop bleeding when it needs to. This makes it difficult when labor begins because you are more likely to lose a lot of blood to start with. In some cases, if the blood is not able to be stopped, you may even need to have a blood transfusion.
- Postpartum Depression—in some cases, you may experience more severe postpartum depression if you are suffering from anemia.
- Having a baby born with anemia—depending on how severe the anemia is, it could begin to affect the blood of the baby. Everything that you take in or that occurs to you could affect the baby if it goes on long enough. If you are not taking care of the anemia early on, the baby is not going to get the oxygen or other nutrients through the blood that are needed and over time they may begin to notice some issues with anemia when they are first born.
- Developmental delays in the baby—this is not as likely to happen when iron is the cause of the anemia, but when you are suffering from anemia thanks to vitamin B12 or folic acid deficiency, it is possible to experience birth defects in a baby who would otherwise be considered normal. Of course, being a bit deficient is not going to be the end of the world, but if you are

severely lacking in one or both of these nutrients, some extreme measures may need to be taken to avoid any birth defects or other issues.

- Birth defects—in some severe cases, especially when you are short on the folic acid that your baby needs, it is possible that birth defects can occur. Some of the ones you would need to be concerned with include those of the brain and the spine as well as issues with the neural tubes of the baby.

As you can see, these are not issues that are much fun to deal with and simply by eating the right foods and taking a prenatal vitamin, you will be able to prevent. Make sure that you get early testing if you feel that you are suffering from anemia in order to avoid the issues listed above.

Food Nutrition

One of the best ways that you are going to be able to avoid anemia during your pregnancy is to eat a good diet. The most common form of anemia during this time is one caused by iron deficiency, but luckily, there are a lot of foods that contain this nutrient if you are just eating the right foods.

While this seems easy enough, those who have been pregnant before know that it is not always as easy as it seems to sit down and eat something that is healthy for you. It may always seem like the baby wants you to eat unhealthy foods, like pastas, pizzas, and ice cream. These do not contain the iron that you need though so they will need to be avoided. Of course, splurging a bit while pregnant is not going to do a lot of harm, but you should not make this the norm when you are pregnant.

Eating iron rich foods is the best way to get a lot of iron in your system in a short amount of time in a natural way. Plus most of the foods that have tons of iron are also going to have a lot of other nutrients that are good for your body as well. Some of the foods you should consider trying out for the health of you and your baby in terms of iron are:

Your greens—the dark and leafy ones are the best because they are the ones that will contain the most iron in them, but some of the other options are going to be good standbys, as well, if you need them. Some options that fit into this category would include kale, collard greens, and spinach

Dried fruits—nothing is better for your body, as well as for that sweet tooth when you are pregnant, than fruit. And dried fruit is perfect if you would like to get some extra iron into the body during pregnancy. Some options here would include figs, raisins, prunes, and apricots.

Beans—beans have gotten a bad reputation over the years, but it is a good way to get in some extra iron, as well as fiber to fill you up. You do not have to sit there and eat the beans straight out of the can though. There are plenty of recipes that can include beans or you can add them to your own personal favorite soups and other recipes

Eggs—the yolk is where all of the iron is at and these are a great way to gain some extra protein to help with any morning sickness, as well. You can cook up a nice omelet in the morning or have some eggs in a salad in order to get that extra iron that your body needs.

Black strap molasses—think of this as the sweet tooth quencher of your pregnancy, as well as, a great way to get the iron that your body needs to stay healthy during this time. Add this to some of your drinks or a few meals in order to get more iron while also working on those cravings for something that is sweet.

Meat—meats, such as, liver and all red meats, are great while you are pregnant. They have the protein that you need in order to fill up, keep away the morning sickness, and prevent you from running low on iron. Many vegetarians and vegans have issues with their iron content during pregnancy because they are not eating this important form of nutrition during this time. Make sure to have at least a few servings of this each day for the best results

Cereals—walking down the grocery store aisles you are sure to see that most of the cereals that you can purchase now have cereals that contain extra iron in them. These have been fortified with the iron, which means that they are not naturally full of that much iron but that it has been added in. This is still going to be just fine for your needs because you will be getting the extra iron no matter what. Having a bowl of this for your breakfast is a great way to ensure that you are getting in some extra iron.

Prenatal vitamins—no matter how good your diet may be during pregnancy, it is still recommended that you take a prenatal vitamin. These are critical to helping you to get the nutrients that you need. If you take in too much of a vitamin, it is just going to be eliminated from the body so there is no harm done. When you are picking out a prenatal vitamin, take into consideration whether it has enough iron, folic acid, and vitamin B12 to keep you healthy and to avoid anemia. It is also good if the vitamin has a lot of other nutrients to keep your body nice and strong.

These are just a few of the different options that you have available in order to eat the nutrients that the body will need to have during pregnancy. Pregnancy is a unique time in your life where you will need to take in many more nutrients than you are used to and eating a healthy diet is the best way for you to do that.

Just make sure that during your pregnancy you are eating lots of fruits, vegetables, lean meats, and dairy products and you are sure to get all of the nutrients, including iron to prevent anemia, that you need in order to have a healthy pregnancy.

Treatment And Prevention

Treating and preventing anemia are important during your pregnancy if you want to have a healthy time of it and a healthy baby. Luckily, both parts are pretty easy to accomplish and are not going to include a lot of work. These will both be discussed below.

Treatment

If you already have developed anemia during the pregnancy, you are going to have several courses that you can take in order to deal with it. Hopefully, the anemia is caught early on so that you are able to do treatments that are easy and will not take up too much of your time. The first course of action that your doctor is going to prescribe for you includes taking a supplement that contains plenty of iron as well as some folic acid. Usually, your prenatal vitamins will be enough to deal with this, but if not, you may have to take an additional supplement.

You will need to take the supplement for a certain amount of time, determined by your doctor. After this time, you may get another blood test to check and see if the anemia is being helped. If it is, you will probably be prescribed to continue taking the supplement for the rest of the pregnancy and perhaps for some time afterwards. If the treatment is not working well, other courses of action may need to be considered.

Just like with the folic acid and iron deficiencies, if you are short on vitamin B12, your doctor is going to recommend that you start to take a supplement for this particular nutrient. You may also be recommended to take on more animal foods into the diet. This would be recommended in most cases if you are vegan or vegetarian and do not get these products much in the first place. Some of the foods that you will need to add into the diet in this cause would be more dairy products, eggs, and meat.

In some cases, your doctor may refer you to a specialist to determine the right steps that you need to take. This kind of specialist is known as a Hematologist and they are the ones who are able to specialize in blood issues and anemia. Depending on how severe the anemia is and when it is first discovered, your Hematologist may see you several times throughout the pregnancy to help deal with and manage your anemia.

Preventing the Anemia

A better course of action for you to take is to learn how to prevent anemia before it even happens. Luckily, it is usually pretty easy for you to prevent anemia if you take the right steps ahead of time. Some of the ways that you will be able to work at preventing anemia in your pregnancy include:

Eating enough iron—you should have a diet that is high in iron and is well balanced. There are a lot of options that fit into this category including fish, meat, and poultry, as well as, a variety of beans and other vegetables.

Enjoy foods that have some vitamin C in them—this might not sound like it is going to work if you are dealing with anemia, but the vitamin C is a great way to help with absorbing the iron you are taking in. You are never going to get any use of the iron if you are not able to get it to absorb into the body and this vitamin helps the iron to do this. Make sure to pick some fruits with a lot of vitamin C, such as citrus fruits, kiwis, tomatoes, and strawberries, to help out during the pregnancy. Eat the foods that are high in vitamin C near the same time as eating the foods that are rich in iron so that you can instantly absorb the iron that you are consuming.

Choose foods with lots of folic acid—this is going to help you to prevent folic acid deficiency which can be the leading cause of birth defects in your baby. Luckily there are many foods that will fit into this category including many of the ones that are already listed in this book.

Follow instructions on supplements and prenatal vitamins—these are often a great way for you to get in some of the nutrients that you are not able to get through just diet, or at least they are a good way to have a safety blanket. But it is still a good idea to talk to your doctor about them first to ensure that you are taking one that has the right amount of folic acid and iron that your body is going to need.

Vegan and vegetarian—those who follow this kind of diet are going to need to take some special precautions because they are already missing out on some important food groups that help during pregnancy. Just because you are pregnant does not mean that you need to give up the lifestyle and diet choices you have made, it just means that you will need to be careful to ensure that you are getting the nutrients that you and your baby need during this important time. If you are following one of these diets, you should discuss this right away with your doctor to determine the right course of action for your needs.

Dealing with anemia does not have to be a difficult thing, as long as you take the right precautions, get tested early, and start to deal with the problem right away. The main issues are going to arise if the anemia is not caught or you are not taking care of the issue and leaving it untreated long after it should be. But for those who have mild anemia or those who are able to catch it in the early stages and do something about it, you will find that it is not that difficult to take care of this condition. Early diagnosis and routine checkups with your doctor can make this much easier to deal with.

Chapter Seven: Vegans, Vegetarians, and Iron Deficiency

One popular reason that many people might suffer from iron deficiency anemia is a plant-based diet. This lifestyle choice may be undertaken with the best of intentions, but without a real knowledge of nutrition and care for the body and its nutritional needs, a vegan and vegetarian diet may leave you lacking the desired nutrients that promote healthy growth and development.

Vegans are especially prone to the limitations that their diets result in, and iron deficiencies coupled with vitamin B12, folate, and calcium deficiencies may all arise as a serious result of irresponsible diet planning. While it is possible to continue on a path of plant-based eating, it can only be done if care and consideration are taken into the consumption of foods that are diverse and rich in vitamins and minerals that support the metabolic system and other important aspects of the body.

Unfortunately, it is a lot less common for vegans and vegetarians born in North America to have proper nutrition, as the diets that ensure healthy results, such as plant-based diets in countries rich in fruits, vegetables, and whole grains, are not as readily available. The Standard American Diet, also known as the SAD diet, does not prepare most people for a healthy execution of the vegan or vegetarian diets, so one must be entirely self-motivated when it comes to seeing to a nutritionally sound way of approaching this lifestyle.

Iron, Folate, and Vitamin B12 Deficiencies in Vegan and Vegetarian Diets

The sad fact of the matter is that people who live on a plant-based diet for a long time may be neglecting a serious need. Iron, vitamin B12, and folates are generally combined in animal-based foods and consumed together to ensure healthy metabolic systems and blood production. However, once a person decides to embark upon a plant-based diet, that easy source of iron, folates and vitamin B12 are gone.

Without proper nutrition and careful supplementation, nutritional deficiencies can and will occur. The longer you go without diagnosing a nutritional deficiency, the harder it becomes to reverse the results of these dangerous limitations of the body. For example, a vitamin B12 deficiency can permanently reduce brain functioning, harm the memory, and cause lasting damage to the nerves.

These deficiencies are common and often ignored. However, just because we are surviving on the diets that we are on does not mean that our bodies are thriving. And issues later on will crop up, as a result, sometimes even leading to premature death. Take care of your body now rather than suffering later.

How Much Vitamin B12 and Folate Do We Need?

Unless we are deficient in vitamin B12, the amount of this vitamin that we need is surprisingly small. The FDA suggests that we need only consume about 2.4 micrograms of vitamin B12 daily.

What many vegans forget to take into consideration is that the vitamin B12 and folate compound actually work together as part of the B-complex vitamins. Whether or not we consume folic acid won't matter if we aren't receiving enough vitamin B12 to activate it.

It is generally rare to have a vitamin B12 deficiency, but if a plant-based lifestyle is your choice, it is sadly simple. As we age, however, this deficiency can become a lot more common, as our bodies begin to have a hard time absorbing vitamin B12 the older we get. Instead of absorbing the vitamin B12 we receive, we end up eliminating it as a waste product.

As for folates, the recommended daily allowance is as follows:

- Children six months old and younger: 65 micrograms per day
- Children seven months to 12 months of age: 80 micrograms per day
- Children one to three years of age: 150 micrograms per day
- Children four to eight years of age: 200 micrograms per day

- Children nine to 13 years of age: 300 micrograms per day
- Children 14 years of age and older: 400 micrograms per day
- Women who are nursing: 500 micrograms per day
- Women who are pregnant: 600 micrograms per day

If a deficiency is found, your doctor may recommend a higher dosage of a folate supplement. Make sure to follow instructions closely in order to combat folate deficiencies before any long-term harm is done to your body or mind.

Symptoms of Vitamin B12 Deficiency

There are many complications that can arise from a vitamin B12 deficiency. Make sure that you are on top of all of your symptoms and consult a doctor and nutritionist when experiencing symptoms of a vitamin B12 deficiency. Remember, this type of deficiency can make it difficult, if not impossible, to absorb enough iron in the body. Our bodies are made up of systems that work together to function and if one or more areas fail to thrive, that can have a lasting impact on our bodies and minds.

Symptoms of vitamin B12 deficiency include:

- Megaloblastic anemia
- Fatigue

- Pale skin
- Weakness
- Heart palpitations
- Constipation
- Gas
- Vision loss
- Memory loss
- Behavioral changes
- Loss of appetite
- Shortness of breath
- Nerve issues
- Tingling in the arms or legs
- Depression
- Confusion
- Diarrhea
- Shortness of breath

Vitamin B12 deficiency can generally be treated, even if you choose to maintain your vegan or vegetarian lifestyle. If you are not absorbing vitamin B12 as a result of other health problems, that can also generally be treated. For those suffering from health issues outside of their chosen diet, a lifetime of supplements, injections, and nasal therapies meant to help maintain a balance of vitamin B12 can result in a healthier relationship with vitamin B12 for your body.

If you are vegan or vegetarian, a vitamin B12 deficiency is easy to combat and prevent in the future, simply by making conscious dietary choices to include vitamin B12 into your diet. There are supplements, vitamins, and injections that are available to those deficient in vitamin B12 and you should take care to include foods that have been fortified with vitamin B12 so that you do not become deficient in vitamin B12 again.

While these are great ways to work through the symptoms of a vitamin B12 deficiency, there is a sad and lasting problem that cannot always be mended. If the vitamin B12 deficiency was caught too late and caused nerve damage to your body, that is irreversible.

If you suspect you may be suffering from a vitamin B12 deficiency, do everything in your power to get a handle on it and reverse the effects before it is too late. Consult a doctor and be careful when making dietary choices in the future.

Chapter Eight: Foods and Iron Supplements

Natural Foods To Boost Your Hemoglobin Level

You can increase the level of blood in your body simply by your diet. If paid attention on diet, one can increase the hemoglobin level in body. So here are some natural foods to boost your hemoglobin level in body.

Beetroot:

Beetroot or beet is a superfood for iron deficiency. Beetroot is filled with iron content. You can have it either raw or a glass of juice. It fulfills the need of iron in human's body. If someone drinks juice of beetroot daily for a month, the person can experience significant amount of improvement in body. This fruit has several health benefits. People who are fighting from anemia, has a good option for them. If you are having beetroot in a form of juice then you can get maximum benefit from it. If you don't like simple juice then you can add lemon juice and black salt in it. You can experience improvement in health in just one month.

Pomegranate:

Pomegranate is also one of the fruit rich in iron. It regulates blood flow in the body. People who are suffering from weakness or iron deficiency can add into its daily diet. You can either have it as raw seeds or a glass of juice. Both will benefit you in iron deficiency. One can add into its daily diet for avoiding any illness related to blood. This fruit is recommended in blood related illness. It has also other benefits. It is also good for heart. If someone eat pomegranate for a month then the person can expect increased level of hemoglobin up to some points. Add this fruit into your daily diet for maximum benefit.

Tomatoes:

Tomatoes contain vitamin C as main content. But tomatoes absorb iron content easily. Eating 2 tomatoes daily can easily increase the iron content in your body. You can have it either raw or a glass of juice. You can also add it into curries or soups too. Adding tomatoes into your daily diet can improve the iron need in your body. It absorbs iron in our body easily. You can expect few points increment in hemoglobin level in just one month.

Beans:

Beans are good source of iron and vitamins. It is considered that beans are high iron content. It will help you to fight anemia. You need to cook it properly to gain maximum benefit. You can have it as salad or by adding it into curry. One cup of boiled beans is recommended to fulfill daily requirements of iron. You can have it either in your food or eat it with some seasoning to enjoy it.

Meat:

By eating an iron rich diet can produce RBCs count. Adding meat in to your diet such as beef, kidney and liver can fulfil the requirement of iron in your body. You can see significant amount of improvement in your RBCs count.it will help you to fight with anemia. It is a great source of iron. Within few weeks you will see greater improvement in your hemoglobin level. If you are a non-vegetarian then you can fulfil your iron requirement with seafood kidneys, liver and beef. You can also have red meat into your diet because it is the great source of iron.

Watermelon:

It is the most delicious, refreshing and nutritious food. One can expect a little amount of improvement in RBCs count by adding it into daily diet. This food also contains iron. You can have it either as raw or a glass of juice. Adding it into your daily diet will help you to improve your hemoglobin levels. This fruit is available only in summers. It also has several other benefits too. It is delicious fruit to add into your daily diet in summer for improvement in RBCs count.

Green leafy vegetables:

Green leafy vegetables those are dark in color are full with iron content. Vitamins and minerals that are present in green leafy vegetables are liable for production of blood. Spinach is a superfood that cures many illnesses. People who are fighting from anemia should add green leafy vegetables into their daily diet for speedy recovery. Green leafy vegetables such as spinach, kale and collard greens are a good source of iron. One should consume it daily for daily requirement of iron. One cup of it will give enough iron for daily dose. You can either add it into your salad or have one cup of boiled vegetables into your food. You can put it in your curry too.

Amla:

Amla is a good source of iron. Eating an amla everyday can improve your hemoglobin levels and cure anemia too. You can have it either raw or with honey. You can make murabba (pickle) of it. You can take murabba with food to avoid any blood related illness. It will help you to fight with anemia. Taking an amla everyday can fulfil the requirement of daily iron. You can have it as juice with water adding honey into it. You can prepare it at home too. Take 100 ml of amla juice,100 ml of water and 1 teaspoon of honey into it. Mix it well and drink it. It will improve your hemoglobin level in just one month if followed properly.

Apple:

An apple contains Vitamin C which absorbs iron in body slowly. An apple or two can do anemia at bay. Taking two apples in a day fulfils daily requirement of iron. It also improves overall health of a person. You can have it as raw or you can make shake of it. You can mix it with other fruits. Apple is a great fruit. It gives several other health benefits if consumed daily.

Nuts:

Nuts have high iron content. Among all the nuts, pistachios have the most iron content. It is an ideal healthy snack. Nuts like almonds and cashews have also iron content. But pistachios have 4 times more iron content than almonds and cashews. If you are fighting with anemia or lacking RBCs count and your doctor advised you to take iron then you can go for variety of nuts. It will work as iron supplement for you. Handful of nuts (different varieties in nuts) can do wonder job for you. Your daily iron requirement can be fulfilled by taking nuts in your daily diet. It keeps in check your overall health too. It has immense benefits. You can't ignore the benefits of nuts.

Eggs:

Eggs also contains iron content. They may not contain large amount of iron but a little can also give you benefit for a day. One or two egg can fulfill your daily requirement of iron. If you are fighting from anemia then an egg or two can help you in it.

Dates:

Dates is sweet and delicious fruit. Dates are rich in iron which are responsible for production of RBCs count. Having two or three dates in a day will keep anemia away. If you are fighting with anemia then you can take 2-3 dates as afternoon or evening snacks. It will help you to fight with anemia. All you need to have 2-3 dates daily. You will feel significant amount of improvement in your health. You can take it as snacks. You can take this with milk too. It will boost iron levels in the body.

Raisins:

Raisins are great source of iron and vitamin C. Dried form of fruits have more iron than fresh fruits. Vitamin C in raisin is responsible for absorption of iron in body while iron is responsible for increasing hemoglobin level in the body. Raisins have more iron than any other fresh fruit.

There are also some foods that are iron rich. You can go for fish, apricots, broccoli, tofu, dark chocolate, oats, dried peas, white rice and potatoes. If you have followed these foods into your diet, you can definitely improve your hemoglobin levels in just one month. All you have to do is just include these foods into your diet. If you want to increase your hemoglobin levels naturally then here are some top iron rich foods which are mentioned above. Without any medications, you can increase your level of iron in the body and your body will say thank you for that.

All About Iron Supplements

The unfortunate fact of the matter is that with any diet that is low in anything, supplements are going to be the best way to receive more nutrition. It is almost guaranteed that if you are struggling with iron deficiency anemia, you will be prescribed an iron supplement to help you to cope with this inadequacy in your diet. However, there are many questions and concerns that you might have when it comes to taking a supplement to improve your health. This section will go through the most common questions associated with iron supplements.

Ferrous Versus Ferric Iron

It is hard to tell which type of iron supplement you should be taking without medical intervention. There are two main types of iron supplements available and while each have their own benefits, it is important to consult a doctor before attempting to treat iron deficiency anemia with supplements.

The majority of iron supplements are made of ferrous iron, simply because it is a little bit easier on the body and can be absorbed better. There are three subcategories of ferrous iron. Ferrous fumarate, ferrous sulfate, and ferrous gluconate are most often prescribed to those who are suffering from an iron deficiency. This is because they are generally the fastest way to introduce iron into a body that is suffering from iron deficiency.

Unfortunately for our bodies, ferric iron is less often prescribed because it does not get absorbed as easily. Our bodies have a hard time breaking ferric iron down into the form that is easiest for us to absorb – ferrous iron. This may be dangerous because an inability to break down iron can lead to iron poisoning. If you are prescribed ferric iron, supplements made with iron citrate are recommended, as this is the easiest form of ferric iron for our bodies to utilize.

What to Look for in Ferrous Iron Supplements

Ferrous iron supplements come in liquid form, capsules, tablets, drops, and extended-release formulas. It is important to look at the "Elemental Iron" amount in an iron supplement before deciding on which is right for you. It is generally agreed that adults with iron deficiency anemia need to receive somewhere between 60 and 200 milligrams of elemental iron.

How to Take Iron Supplements

Whenever embarking upon a new type of medication, there are some guidelines and rules that will apply. Iron supplements are no exception. In order to receive the full benefit of your iron supplement, there are a few rules to follow.

First of all, never take iron supplements with tea, milk, or other dairy products. Unfortunately, calcium has a negative impact on iron absorption and can prevent the desired effects of iron supplementation. It is also important not to combine iron with antacids for similar reasons. You should make sure to time the intake of calcium and antacids so that you do not take them within two hours of taking your iron supplements.

Instead of taking your iron with a glass of milk, it is recommended that you take your iron supplement with orange juice. Orange juice is full of vitamin C, which aids in the absorption of iron in the body. This combination will ensure that as much of the iron supplement makes it into your body as possible.

It is also recommended that iron supplements be taken on an empty stomach. Iron supplements may cause a little bit of stomach upset, so if you really need to, you could take iron supplements with a piece of bread. However, the rule of thumb is to make sure you haven't eaten at least two hours before taking your iron supplement. This ensure that your body is getting as much iron from the supplement as possible. Taking supplements with food can decrease the amount of iron absorbed by up to 60%. This will inevitably result in a longer duration of needing to take iron supplements.

If you are taking your iron supplement in liquid form, make sure that you are mixing it thoroughly in your drink and drinking it with a straw. Unfortunately, iron supplements tend to stain the teeth, even darkening the stool, so it is recommended that a straw is used when taking the supplement. Be sure to brush your teeth thoroughly after drinking a liquid supplement to prevent staining the teeth.

Make sure that you are consuming a lot of liquids when you take your iron supplements. The liquids will help to off-set the common issue of constipation that occurs with iron supplements. Over-the-counter stool softeners are safe to pair with iron supplements if this is an issue for you.

Side Effects of Iron Supplements

As with anything, iron supplements can sometimes be dangerous, particularly if they are taken in doses that are too large for your body to absorb properly. This is why it is so important to have a relationship with a caring and responsible medical practitioner during the duration of treatment for an iron deficiency.

Side effects of iron supplements vary on the inconvenient to the extreme. It is common for stool to look dark, even black, when taking these supplements, but it is dangerous if you notice that stool has blood in it or is tar-like in appearance. Consult your doctor about this immediately and ask about changing your iron supplement if these symptoms occur. You should also mention if you have experienced symptoms such as nausea or stomach upset upon the consumption of iron supplements.

More hazardous issues may occur if you are taking too much iron for your body to handle. For example, you can begin to feel feverish or suffer from headaches, weakened pulse, low blood pressure, chills, and dizziness. Fluid may begin to build up in your lungs and it is even possible to go into a coma if you overdose on iron supplements. This risk is heightened for those who suffer from hemochromatosis, a hereditary condition that causes the body to take in far more iron than it needs. Be careful and always keep your doctor in the loop before making decisions about consumption of iron supplements.

How Long Will It Take for Supplements to Make a Difference?

When we realize that we have a deficiency, it is usually alarming enough that we hope to find an immediate cure. We may even feel impatient to fix the problem right away and feel like the time it takes to heal isn't fast enough.

However, it can take time for the body to begin producing the proper amount of hemoglobin that it needs to produce large, healthy red blood cells that can carry enough oxygen to the body. This is especially true if you have been anemic for a long time without diagnosis or treatment. Patience is the name of the game when it comes to treating anemia.

If the anemia is not too extreme, iron supplements may be able to begin to implement new red cell growth and circulation within a week. Once that begins to happen, upon the initial reception of the iron supplements, hemoglobin should start to rise in a matter of two to three weeks.

Depending on the severity of your anemia, treatment may take as little as eight weeks before the body's red blood cell count and the quality of the hemoglobin are back to normal. However, supplements remain a crucial part of the treatment process for up to two months after the fact, just to make sure the body has enough iron stored for future use. It is important to make sure that the body won't become easily depleted again.

Chapter Nine: Do's and Don'ts to Improve Blood Circulation

Symptoms of Poor Blood Circulation

Once your brain stops receiving the amount of oxygen it needs to properly function, you could experience brain hypoxia. Symptoms of this brain hypoxia include memory loss, difficulty concentrating, loss of motor skills or movement of your body, and seizures. You are also at risk for a stroke.

Another indicator of poor circulation is a pale, sallow look to the skin. Someone with poor circulation will appear sickly, with a lack of healthy color in their face. This is due to the lack of blood flow to the capillaries under the skin. In addition to the lack of healthy color to the face, there is also an early onset of wrinkles and sagging skin. The premature aging of skin is just one of the visual symptoms of poor circulation. Smoking can contribute to poor circulation and premature aging of the skin. Contributing to a poor aesthetic could also be a lack of exercise, poor diet, poor skin care (try dry brushing), and a diet high in sodium.

Another visual symptom is varicose veins. Varicose veins have been plaguing more than just your Aunt Myrtle since humans began to walk upright. The veins most commonly affected are those in your lower extremities. They are caused by the failure of the valves in the veins that prevent blood from flowing backward into the vein. The fluid collects and creates bulging, often painful, protruding vessels. Your physician may recommend treatments ranging from lifestyle changes to surgery to resolve and prevent varicose veins. The lifestyle changes all focus around improving blood circulation, including losing weight.

Hair loss is another symptom those with poor circulation may experience. Hair follicles become deprived of required oxygen and nutrients to sustain healthy hair growth, causing the hair follicle to die off. Males who were diagnosed with male pattern baldness had a scalp blood flow three times lower than males with full heads of hair. You can stimulate more hair growth or prevent more hair loss, by increasing blood flow a few different ways. Scalp massage (using your hands or another's hands) not only increases blood flow but also reduces stress and tension that additionally can cause hair loss. Brushing your hair twice a day with a bristle brush will also stimulate and bring more blood flow to the scalp.

You can add weight gain and obesity to the list as well. This automatically puts you at risk for diabetes, hypertension, and heart disease. This is a hefty group of ailments to add to the mix! This could mean a lifetime of medicines, heart attacks, and expensive hospitalizations. Hypertension can also cause kidney failure as a result of damage to the arteries around the kidneys, as well as loss of vision.

You may also notice that your hands and feet are often cold or tingly in winter, sometimes even experiencing numbness, based on the severity of the blood flow restriction. Female is more likely to have cold feet than male as male generally has better blood circulation than female. That is why in generally speaking, middle age woman tends to get sick easier than middle age man.

Energy levels are greatly affected as well. Experiencing lethargy and shortness of breath is common in people who suffer from poor circulation. No matter how much they sleep, they just feel tired during the day. If you don't have the energy inside your body, how do you do a proper job at work? Lethargy will get you nowhere near your promotion or higher salary. Moreover, the impact on how they are able to enjoy their life is measurable, affecting daily activities from trips to the grocery store, family outings, and sex life.

With symptoms like these mounting, a person could fall victim to depression very easily. Dealing with multiple maladies, a decline in physical appearance, and not able to perform in life at full capacity, will eventually take a toll on mental health. As you look at the mirror and see an unhealthy appearance, you feel more depress and it will affect your health even more, and you are going in a vicious cycle. If you do not treat yourself right, at some point, you might feel so afraid that you do not look at the mirror anymore. The decline in physical appearance is an indirect symptom of the effects of poor circulation. Tending to your declining mental health along with other mounting health conditions will result in more money spent on medications and doctor visits. There is also the possibility of forever altering your brain chemistry with anti-depressants so that you may depend on the medications for life.

If you're not exercising or maintaining good blood circulation, you can expect more frequent visits to the doctor. Why spend money and time on doctors for your weak body while you can just spend time on exercise for your strong body? The money you could be spending on a new bicycle to ride or a gym membership ends up being spent on the health issues you have developed. This doesn't include the time missed from work, where you could put yourself at risk of being let go. No matter how hard you work, if you look weak and pale, your boss will never promote you in higher position. Even if you are a manager which lead a team of staff, your team just won't look up to you and follow your order. Please remember, people always look up to leader with strong characteristics with strong physical body. Even though many people dislike Donald Trump, he is able to demonstrate his power with his strong characteristics as a President of United States. But just imagine would he be the President if he looks sick and in need of medical supply? The answer certainly is "No". Therefore, guard your body well as your first priority, if your immune system is compromised, you must do something about this before your health declines even further! Prevention is better than cure!

Adequate sleep each night is paramount to support a healthy body and mind. Sleep apnea, insomnia, and three times the likelihood of developing hypertension are all possibilities that can happen to a person when they are sleep deprived. Poor blood circulation directly effects quality and length of sleep time and can result in any one of the mentioned sleep conditions.

How to Improve Blood Circulation

Now that you have more in-depth knowledge of anemia as a result of poor blood circulation, it's time to learn different ways to increase your blood flow to improve your health and youthful appearance well into later life.

Many of the simple treatments involve the use of heat. Vessels expand upon exposure to heat, increasing blood circulation in the general area. Here are some simple, yet effective ways of treating and avoiding poor blood circulation:

Vitamin C

Eat foods high in Vitamin C. It is a natural blood thinner, which allows the blood to flow more unrestricted and easily through your veins and capillaries. Vitamin C also promotes the production of collagen for glowing, youthful skin, and boosts immunity. Foods with a naturally high Vitamin C content include citrus fruits, strawberries, red bell peppers, pineapple (more Vitamin C than an orange!), kiwi, guava, brussels sprouts, kohlrabi, papaya, and kale. A simple change in diet can start improving your circulation before the day is over today! Consuming more fruits and vegetables high in Vitamin C will also deliver weight loss results, an added bonus of a healthy diet change.

Omega 3 Fatty Acids

Eat foods high in Omega 3 fatty acids. These essential fatty acids support the cardiovascular system. Our bodies do not produce Omega 3 fatty acids on their own and they thus must be obtained through foods we consume. Foods high in Omega3 include Salmon and other fatty fishes, flaxseed oil, chia seeds, tofu, spinach, grass-fed beef, avocados, and navy beans. There are many resources with more extensive lists of food items rich in Omega 3 fatty acids. These fatty acids block multiple inflammation pathways in your cells and play a part in helping with blood clotting. Omega 3 fatty acids also help regulate our heart rhythm. Krill oil is a recommended supplement over fish oil because it is easier to absorb due to its attachment to phospholipids. There is less belching associated with krill oil than there was reported as common with fish oil. Omega 3 can be found in foods such as hemp, chia seeds, flaxseed, and a few others, but none of these foods contain DHA and EPA, that aids in fighting mental and physical diseases.

Supplements

Take supplements on a regular basis. If you are an on-the-go person and you find it a challenge to prepare and include all the healthy food you should in your diet, supplements can offer a secondary source of essential vitamins and minerals. An alternative to costly medications, supplements are an affordable way to help support proper blood circulation. Plant sterols aid in the elimination of cholesterol consumed in your diet. But please do not overdose. Overdose of any supplements or medicine will damage your liver permanently. As the liver is a vital organ that plays a main role in detoxification, protein synthesis, glycogen storage and decomposition of red cells, so please do not overdose. I said this twice because some people worry about their health so much that they overdose and they died because of cirrhosis (dysfunction of liver due to long term damage).

Lycopene

Lycopene has strong antioxidant properties. The function of antioxidants is to prevent and stop cell damage by inhibiting the oxidation of cells. Lycopene is found to reduce the risk factor of a heart attack or stroke by 3x's vs. people who had lower levels of lycopene in their systems. Hawthorn extract causes vascular dilation and in turn, better blood circulation. In recent studies, regular use of hawthorn extract over at least 15 weeks reduced blood pressure.

Resveratrol

Resveratrol is a powerful antioxidant found in many fruits and vegetables, but taking a supplement to get the maximum benefit of enhanced cardiac function may be easier for you. Bee pollen is a widely-used supplement containing rutin that works by strengthening your blood vessels and prevents the buildup of white blood cells in your arteries. It also aids in preventing blood clots that could alternatively end up causing a cardiac event or stroke.

Heat Your Body

Use heat. Heat expands your blood vessels. This can include hot showers, baths, saunas, hot tubs, infrared light, and heating pads. None of these tools need to be exceedingly hot. A small increase in temperature will cause your blood vessels to expand. That's why Chinese love having saunas while Japanese love having a hot spring. Both saunas and hot spring has the same principal to provide better blood circulation to people. A natural hot spring is even better for your skin because the mineral in the water has great benefits to your skin as the mineral can be easily absorbed by your skin in heated water. Japanese girls have smooth skin because they love hot spring. Infrared light effectively improves blood circulation as much as exercise, and aids in pain relief and healing of wounds and injuries. It is widely used in sports medicine due to the efficiency and speed at which it gets players back on the field. Saunas are also a treatment proven to have coronary benefits, normalizing blood pressure, and increasing blood flow to your muscles. A sauna session just one time to two times a week can make vast improvements in blood circulation. You may want to avoid saunas if you have existing blood pressure issues. Applying a heating pad to the tops of your feet. Once your blood has traveled to the bottom of your extremities, it has to fight gravity to get back up to your heart again. If your vessels are constricted, this makes the task even more difficult. If you suffer from continually cold feet and hands, applying a heating pad to the top of your feet where your skin is thin and many large veins are present will expand the vessels and make the process of delivering blood back up to the heart easier for your body.

Heat Your Feet

Heat your feet everyday! Making sure you keep your feet warm increases peripheral blood flow. Having cold feet could be a result of cold weather, cold floors in your home, a symptom of a circulation restrictive health condition such as Raynaud's disease or diabetes. In Chinese, they think that the benefits of put your feet in hot water are similar to eating expensive food with high nutrition value. Keeping your feet warm can be used as a preventative measure to ensure better blood circulation on a regular basis, or as a counteractive measure, once coldness has set in. You do not need to spend a lot of money of supplements and food if your budget is limited, heating your feet don't cost much. Some of the methods of keeping your feet warm include; using your own metabolic rate to warm up your feet while they are covered in very warm socks or down slippers, soaking your feet in a warm pot of water, wrap them with a heating pad. Heating pad is useful because you can control and keep consistent heat on your feet for any length of time, applying a hot water bottle, or wrapping your feet and lower extremities in an electric blanket. The temperature of your feet affects your whole body, causing vessel constriction as cooler blood is circulated. Studies have shown that having chronically cold feet can also increase your risk of catching a cold because of vessel constriction in the nose, which decreases the amount of white blood vessels available to fight off a common cold.

Exercise

Doing exercise regularly. Just 30 minutes a day of exercise will produce profound positive changes within your body. There are many different forms of exercise that you can do, even for those who have limited physical abilities. Getting enough exercise does not have to cost any money. Outside of the typical gym membership, yoga classes, spinning classes and Pilates, there are many other activities you can easily integrate into your daily routine. Throwing a football in the backyard with your kids, playing a couple of games of driveway basketball, going for a bike ride with your family or friends, or just a brisk walk around the block, can make noticeable changes in the way your circulation performs and how your body looks and feels. Athletes and soldiers usually have no problem with blood circulation as they do different kinds of exercise on a regular basis. Not only they have stronger muscles and body, but also they have better skin as the blood under their skin is kept flowing. Athletes have better motivation and usually have positive emotion and self-esteem. Higher level of self-esteem plays an important part of an individual's sex appeal. If impact exercises are out of your reach, stretching is a low-impact, easy way to improve circulation to your organs and muscles. This can be done sitting in a chair, standing, lying in bed, or on the floor. You might try some free instructional videos on the internet, or ask what stretches your physician recommends to avoid injuring yourself.

Sleep At The Right Time

Getting enough exercise also contributes to deeper, longer sleep. Adults should get 7 to 9 hours of sleep each night to achieve maximum benefits, including a period of REM sleep. Sleep deprivation increases blood pressure. Studies have shown that neural cardiovascular control is negatively impacted when subjects did not get enough sleep. While you sleep, your body goes to work repairing blood vessels, your brain and other vital tissues that support your cardiovascular health. Going to bed earlier and ditching "night owl" habits has an even greater impact. Lack of sleep also causes stress. Daily tasks and otherwise easier-to-handle life events seem more difficult to cope with, elevating blood pressure. Adequate sleep supports an important homeostatic function of regulating blood pressure. You may want to look into why your quality of sleep is poor, and implement new sleeping positions and tools to improve your sleep each night. Make sure your neck is not craned and that other body parts are not bent or distorted in a way that may cut off blood circulation. Choosing a blood circulation friendly position to fall asleep in each night can help with a more restful sleep. Consider a new mattress and pillows. It has been found that sleeping on your side is the recommended sleep position. There are many benefits to side-sleeping, two of which are flushing harmful waste from your body via the glymphatic systems, and increasing blood flow to your heart. If you have exhausted all of these options and still have trouble sleeping, try a little more exercise during the day, take a few deep breathe at night in your bed or consult with your physician.

Drink Water To Cleanse Your Body

Drink more water. Not just any water, but hot or warm water in the morning. Many of us enjoy a crisp glass of ice cold water, but if you are trying to increase your blood circulation, it could be counter-productive. Warm water acts in the same ways as the other heat methods, expanding your blood vessels in your digestive tract and aids in the digestion process, better eliminating fats from your meals. This is a beneficial effect vs. cold water which causes the fat to solidify. Just like bacon grease in the pan. Once it cools off, it is solid and white and harder to eliminate from your intestines. Adding fresh squeezed lemon to the water for taste is a healthy way to add some flavor, in addition to turning your glass of warm water into its own super drink. Fresh lemon contains natural enzymes that assist your liver in getting rid of toxins. Rich in flavonoids that increase blood flow circulation, they also pack a punch of Vitamin C. At the very least, drink one glass of warm water each morning, but feel free to add a few more glasses throughout the day and night or with meals to get the most out of this circulation boosting method.

Vitamin D

Soak up the sun! Vitamin D plays a critical role in healthy vasculature. Hypovitaminosis D, or vitamin D deficiency, The muscles in your heart need calcitriol to maintain and build healthy tissues, and vitamin D is converted into calcitriol through a special process. Not only is vitamin D a nutrient, it is also a hormone that plays many important roles in our bodies and circulatory health. Ways to provide your body with vitamin D are direct exposure to sunlight and supplements. Exposing your skin directly to sunlight, which contains the UVB rays that prompt the production of vitamin D in our bodies. There are limited foods that contain vitamin D naturally, so it is easy to become deficient. In order to produce sufficient vitamin D naturally, you need only expose your skin to direct sunlight for about 15 minutes. Getting a sunburn or prolonged sun exposure will not produce more vitamin D. The process happens quickly within your body. Your body can produce between 10,000 and 25,000 IU (International Units) of vitamin D in that short amount of time. If you have darker skin, you may require a few extra minutes of sun exposure than those with pale skin. If you choose to go the supplement route, there are many good quality brands and types to choose from. There are several websites dedicated to testing and providing information on different brands of vitamin D, including which ones to avoid that may contain lead and other harmful elements like mercury, arsenic, and cadmium. Their studies show that the pill type did not affect the quality of the supplement, so choosing between a gelcap, tablet, and capsule makes no difference. Consult with your health care professional on your specific dosing needs. Most adults should not exceed 4,000 IU without a doctor's recommendation.

Feel Happy and Laugh More

Laugh more! Studies have shown that after 15 minutes of viewing a TV show that induced laughter, 70% of the test subjects showed increased cardiovascular blood flow. Laughter produced the same effect as physical exercise without any of the pain and soreness. It also reduces the amount of the stress hormone cortisol. This could be one of the easiest ways to lower your blood pressure and prevent diabetes. People who laughed after eating a meal also had lower blood glucose levels than those who did not laugh.

Laughter lifts the spirits and reduces overall stress. Consider this one of the easiest ways to improve your circulation.

Foot Reflexology / Foot Massage

Try foot massage. Reflexology technically is not "massage" in its practical form. It is a reflex therapy. Foot reflexology is greatly applied in Chinese to cure disease as it would unclog your blood stream in variety of organs. It uses the application of pressure to different reflex points on the body, specifically the feet, head, hands, and ears. It is generally safe, and promotes a state of relaxation and increased blood flow to various parts of the body by applying pressure to the specific points on the bottom of your foot. Each point of your feet related to certain part of your body, if you feel pain when having foot reflexology, it means that you have some problems with certain part of your body and more reflex therapy is required to cure that part of your body. It is proven to aid in the increase of certain body functions by clearing neural pathways. Reflexology helps to increase circulation and deliver more adequate levels of blood and oxygen to your entire body, enabling your body to heal faster and return to more normal metabolic processes.

Swedish Massage

Swedish massage. A full body massage, specifically the Swedish massage, a few times a week lowers blood pressure more than if you were to just relax for that same amount of time. Swedish massage increases circulation without putting undue strain on the heart. It also aids in cleansing the glands and releasing toxins. Swedish massage applies pressure down deep to the muscles, pressing against other deeper muscles and bones, and rubbing in the direction that the blood flows to the heart (effleurage).

Dry Brushing

Dry brushing your skin uses a handheld bristle brush in gentle strokes all over your skin to stimulate blood flow, remove dead cells, and move toxins through the lymphatic system. Dry brushing also makes your skin vibrant with a healthy glow because dead cells are removed, exposing new, healthy skin cells. Typically, you would dry brush your whole body just before you shower, so you can rinse off the loosened dead skin cells. Try dry brushing once a day as a simple way to increase blood flow circulation to your skin.

The DONT'S! Things To Avoid That Reduce Blood Circulation

DON'T: Consume Sugary Drinks, Caffeine, Or Alcohol.

Even adding 1 sugary drink to your daily intake can contribute to weight gain and a 25% greater risk of developing type II diabetes. Caffeine is a stimulant that increases blood pressure. It has been shown to decrease cerebral blood flow by 27%! If you are a regular caffeine beverage drinker and cut out caffeine, you will have increased cerebral blood flow within 30 hours of your last beverage. A very simple change. While consuming 1 alcoholic beverage per day (A glass of wine, for example) can help maintain healthy circulation, drinking alcohol in excess can negatively affect the cells of endothelium and smooth muscle, both of which work to control blood circulation. Alcohol consumption keeps these cells from working properly.

DON'T: Avoid Caffeinated Teas Such As Green Tea, Black Tea, and Matcha

Though rich in antioxidants, these drinks contain caffeine. I have already covered the negative effects of caffeine on your circulatory system. Opt for a caffeine-free version, although finding one at a supplement dispensary that has no caffeine may prove to be a challenge. Daily flaxseed oil capsules also reduce the chances of a heart attack. There are many knowledgeable specialists that can help walk you through the best supplement options for your situation and circulation challenges. The quality of supplements plays a huge role in their performance. Research the origin and purity of the different brands you come across; otherwise, you may just be spending money on old, dead plants in a pill form that offer no nutrition, are hard for your body to break down, and have limited bioavailability.

DON'T: Go Long Periods Of Time Being Stationary

A sedentary lifestyle will first and foremost become your worst enemy in damaging your circulatory system. One in ten cases of heart disease is caused by a lack of exercise. You also increase your risk of developing diabetes and cancer. Lack of exercise causes almost as many deaths as smoking! On days that you do not exercise, your blood pressure increases. After 2 weeks of no exercise, changes to your blood vessels occur. It will take about another week of exercise to reverse these changes and bring your vessels back to a healthy, higher functioning state. When you exercise, your glucose levels remain higher because your muscles and tissues use the sugars you consume for energy. Without regular exercise, your glucose levels will continue to increase. This is particularly dangerous if you have existing diabetes, but can also prime you for developing the dangerous health condition.

DON'T: Walk Around Outside On Cold Days, Or On Cold Floors Inside With Bare Feet Or Flimsy Shoes

Keeping your feet warm is one of the easiest and effective methods you can practice easily on a regular basis to avoid reducing your overall body temperature and restricting peripheral blood flow, and increasing your susceptibility of catching a cold due to the reduction of available white blood cells within your nose that fight off the virus.

DON'T: <u>Smoke!</u>

The dangers and consequences of smoking are endless. I could write an entire other book on the negative effects of smoking on the body. But if you are specifically worried about improving your blood circulation, this would be one of the first things to cut out of your life. Nicotine itself has been shown to grow new blood vessels within our existing vessels, hardening our arteries and promoting more clogging. Smoking affects every vessel in your body. Smoking also causes our brain to go into "fight or flight" mode, triggering the release of stored fats and sugars for 'emergency' situations and immediate use for energy, into your blood stream. This is especially detrimental to anyone with diabetes because it triggers a spike in glucose levels every time you smoke! This is also why smoking curbs your appetite and causes you to crave another cigarette soon after, because you are essentially skipping meals and the release of the stored fats and sugars are "feeding" you. Smoking will prematurely age your skin. There is no reversing aged skin. The only way to keep your youthful look is by preventative care, which includes stopping smoking.

DON'T: Consume High Sodium Foods.

This works doubly well when you couple lowering your sodium intake with adding the foods that increase blood flow to your diet. Sodium causes hardening of your arteries, which leads to high blood pressure. Reducing sodium in your diet takes a little more than not putting salt on your food. You need to look at the nutritional information of your food *before* you add salt, so you know exactly what you are consuming. If you have a health condition such as high blood pressure, the recommended daily amount of sodium intake is 1,500mg per day. If you are relatively healthy, the average person is recommended to stay at or below 2,300mg per day. Sodium plays an important role in our bodies muscle and nerve function and regulation of blood pressure, so eliminating all sodium from your diet is not recommended and can end up causing more severe problems than just poor circulation!

Creating Effective Exercise and Stretching Routines

The heart is the organ that pumps blood around the body, and when you become very active, even for just a minute, you'll realize that it starts to beat faster. This is due to the fact that the amount of oxygen your muscles need to do the work needs to be increased, and the only way to do this is by getting blood to those muscles at a faster rate and at a higher volume. Hence, you realize that you also start to breathe heavier and quicker. This goes to show how much your muscles and your body on the whole depend on oxygenated blood. If oxygenated blood is reduced, then you will not be able to move around in the way that you are used to. Not only will your locomotion be affected, but vital organs such as the liver and your kidneys could be affected as well due to poor blood circulation. Exercise and stretching helps a lot in correcting this problem, and we'll discuss the ways in which it does this and the specific exercises that you could do.

When you exercise regularly, your heart beats at a regular and healthy rate. When your body becomes accustomed to a certain lifestyle, it adjusts to it. So if you exercise regularly, then you will find that your body adjusts to this by building muscle, getting your heart rate up, and raising your metabolism. If it doesn't do this, then it won't be able to handle the strains of your exercises. On the other hand, if you sit around all day, eating junk food and watching Netflix, then your body will just store fat, slow your heart rate down, and lower your metabolism to conserve energy. When your heart rate slows and fat accumulates under your skin and around your organs and arteries, blood flow is restricted, which could potentially cause a host of problems for you in the short and long-term. Get your circulation at a regular level again by making sure that you exercise.

You can get your blood flowing in the way it's meant to be by doing simple 15-minute exercises every day. You don't need to be pressing 500 lbs. to do so. These simple exercises include brisk walking, running, swimming, skipping and kickboxing. These exercises don't involve weights at all but involve just about every muscle in the body, which raises your heart rate and gets your blood flowing. These are generally called cardio exercises, and as the name suggests, these exercises get your heart rate up.

Cardio exercises are great, however, some studies have shown that weight training is the most effective form of exercise to regularize circulation. Not only does weight training improve your heart rate, it improves the way your muscles work as well, and involves the movement of your skeletal system. This helps improve your posture, which greatly improves your circulation. Hence, weight training is like a 2-in-1 treatment for bad blood circulation. If you are not so wild on cardio exercises, then you can do some weight and resistance training as well. This is not for everyone, so ensure that weight training will be suitable for you. It might be a challenge for someone who wants to regularize blood circulation to the extreme sections of their limbs, like their fingers.

With weights, focus on major muscle groups, such as your arms and your legs. But don't forget your core, which is something a lot of people like to forget about (mainly because it hurts so much). Every morning or evening, at home or the gym, focus on one muscle group at a time. So, for example, you could focus on legs on a Monday. The best and simplest leg exercises include squats, lunges and deadlifts. On Tuesday, you could focus on your arms, where you can do bicep curls, arm extensions and rotator cuffs. On Wednesday, you could focus on your chest and back, where you could do simple exercises such as chest presses, push-ups and pull-ups. Finally on Thursday, work on your core, where you could do weighted sit-ups and other core exercises. You don't have to do four days, but it's recommended that you do at least 2, while including cardio on at least one more day. The best thing to do is to have at least four days to work out. Exercising will not only improve your circulation and posture, but will also improve your appearance and your outlook on life.

Finally, remember to stretch. It is important that you stretch before and after you exercise, especially when you have poor blood circulation. Stretching "wakes up" your muscles, and ensures proper blood flow into them. It is possible to injure yourself or even make your situation worse if you do weight training or other exercises with poor blood flow. Also, stretches can help you throughout the day as well, where you are not able to move about as freely as you need to, such as at work. Research has shown that people who do sedentary jobs are at higher risk of getting heart disease and other conditions that are caused by lack of exercises and activity. Sedentary workers often sit in their chairs for 8 or more hours every day, and their health concerns are compounded if they have bad posture.

If you are a sedentary worker, make sure that you do little stretches at regular or irregular intervals throughout the day while you are sitting at your desk. One of these small stretches which you can do is lifting your arms up but having your arms folded, like a bird. Then, rotate them and ensure that your shoulders and arms are all rotating. Do this for at least 20 seconds per session. Another stretch that you can do at work is to rotate your neck. People often leave this out but you'll be amazed at how bad blood circulation affects the blood flow to your neck and to your head. While gently massaging your neck, move your head to the side, slowly drop it and turn to the other side, and back. Ensure that you are gentle, deliberate and slow. In the mornings when you are at home, or even at the gym, you can do a 'cat' stretch. This is where you are on all fours, and raise and lower your back. You can repeat this as many times as possible. After doing exercises involving your arms, you can stretch your arm muscles by putting one arm over the back of your head and letting your hand touch your back, while you use your other hand to grab your elbow. Do this for a few seconds, then switch arms. If you're at work, do this while walking around your cubicle or office, as you will need blood pumping to your legs as well. But the ultimate exercise/stretch of all to get your blood flowing properly again is yoga.

Yoga is an excellent way of stretching your muscles and correcting posture. Being in one stretched position for a long period of time also strengthens your muscles. One of the best poses to use includes the mountain pose, where you stand up straight and have your hands clasped under your chin. Then, take very deep and deliberate breaths. After a few minutes, transition to the chair pose, where you bend your knees and lower your butt close to the floor, like sitting on a chair. Go as low as you can, and remain there for a few minutes while breathing slowly. After this, stand back up, stretch your legs apart as far away as they can, and tilt your torso to one side while having one hand touching the ground and the other hand up in the air. Stay in that position for a few minutes while breathing slowly, then switch sides. After this, bring your legs together again but put one leg out in front of you, getting into a lunging position. Stretch your arms up into the air and remain in this position for a few minutes.

There are many more yoga positions that you could try. You could do this every morning in lieu of cardio and weight training, and it will regularize your blood flow and also make you feel refreshed.

Chapter Ten: Recipes For Anemic People

Breakfast

Charred Black Bean Breakfast Pizza

Preparation Time: 5 minutes

Cooking Time: 10 minutes

Servings: 1

Ingredients:

- 1 c. black beans
- Two halves of wheat pita bread
- 1 c. plain Amatriciana sauce
- 1 c. mint leaves (chopped)
- 1 c. spinach leaves
- Two carrots, sliced
- 1 c. mozzarella cheese (shredded)

Directions:

1. Start with placing black beans in a medium-sized frying pan. Heat this for 4 to 5 minutes stir it in that Time too.
2. When the beans become ready, remove them from the heat and place them aside. Place the halves of

pita bread on a plate, with the help of a spoon, place sauce on both halves of the pita bread.

3. Put these bread halves into the frying pan at low flame heat. 2-3 minutes later, remove it from the heat. Place these halves onto the plate. Place spinach leaves between the halves.
4. Spread beans on the overall dish. Place mint leaves followed with sliced radish. Place slices of mozzarella cheese.
5. Now garnish the plate with sprigs of mint and slices of carrots. Your healthy, delicious breakfast is ready. Just eat it and has a nice day.

Nutrition (Per Serving):

Protein: 87.33 g

Calories: 992

Carbohydrates: 160.92 g

Fat: 4.34 g

Rapini Toast With Fried Egg

Cooking Time: 8 minutes

Servings: 1

Ingredients:

- 2 c. rapini

- 1 tsp. sunflower oil
- 1 red onion (chopped)
- 1 egg
- 2 slice sprouted grain bread

Directions:

1. Start with cutting the rapini into small-sized slices. Pick a pan and place it on the heat. Put oil in it.
2. Add onion and rapini to it and cook until it becomes brown. After this, remove both ingredients from the oil, add an egg, and cook it as much as you want.
3. Alongside the egg, add bread and brown it as well. Place rapini and other roasted vegetables on the top of this toast and enjoy this yummy breakfast.

Nutrition (Per Serving):

Protein: 15.04 g

Calories: 293

Carbohydrates: 23.06 g

Fat: 15.86 g

Veggie Breakfast Sandwiches

Preparation Time: 10 minutes

Cooking Time: 37 minutes

Servings: 3

Ingredients:

- 5 eggs
- 1 small onion (diced)
- 1 tbsp. sunflower oil
- 1 red bell pepper
- 1 green bell pepper
- 1 c. spinach
- 1 tbsp. salt
- 1 tbsp. salt
- 1 c. almond milk
- 3 slices of Feta cheese
- 3 muffins (sliced)

Directions:

1. Start by picking a small frying pan and place it over the heat. Add red, green bell pepper, and onion and fry it for 5 minutes. Preheat the oven to 300°F. After this, add spinach and stir it occasionally.
2. Add pepper and salt and place them aside. Pick a bowl and mix the milk and eggs. Add black pepper and salt. After this, add all vegetables to the egg mixture.
3. Now place vegetables and egg mixture into the pan. Now, bake it at 300°C until the eggs become

cooked. After this, remove the eggs from the oven. Place muffins over a baking sheet.

4. Cut them into slices and place those in the oven until they become fully cooked. Cut the eggs into shapes to fit into the shapes of the muffins. Place the toasted egg onto bread, followed by a slice of cheese.
5. Cover it with another ½ of the muffin. Now your iron-rich sandwiches are ready to eat.
6. Enjoy it and have a nice day. You can store it for 1 month in the freezer.

Nutrition (Per Serving):

Protein: 20.88 g

Calories: 659

Carbohydrates: 59.07 g

Fat: 39.21 g

Orange Almond Ricotta Toast

Preparation Time: 10 minutes

Servings: 1

Ingredients:

- 4 slices whole-wheat bread
- 1 red-fleshed navel orange

- 1 c. almond ricotta (dairy-free)
- 2 tbsp. maple syrup

Directions:

1. Toast the bread in the toaster or frying pan as you like. Make slices of the oranges and put the peel aside.
2. Add almond ricotta to a small bowl. Add maple syrup and mix it with it perfectly. Place toasted slices on the plate and add almond ricotta over it.
3. Add slices of oranges and maple syrup. Your yummy toast is ready. Enjoy it and have a good day.

Nutrition (Per Serving):

Protein: 32.33 g

Calories: 1050

Carbohydrates: 226.55 g

Fat: 7.8 g

Spinach And Brie Oatmeal Bowl

Preparation Time: 5 minutes

Cooking Time: 10 minutes

Servings: 2

Ingredients:

- 1 c. steel-cut oats
- 1 c. skinless chicken breast
- 3-4 spoons olive oil spray
- 2 cloves garlic (minced)
- 1 c. spinach
- 1 egg (large size)
- 1 tbsp. Brie cheese crumbles
- Black pepper
- 2 pt. of salt

Directions:

1. Start by putting the water and stock in the skillet and boiling it. Add oats and cook it on a low flame. Stir it occasionally until the oats absorb the whole moisture.
2. Spray the olive oil in a separate pan and cook the spinach and garlic paste into it for a few minutes. Remove it from the heat.
3. Spray the olive oil in a separate saucepan and place it on the heat. Fry the egg. It depends on you if you want it to be whole fried or ½ fried.
4. Make the thin slices of the chicken breast and fry them in a saucepan until they get brown. After this, remove it from the heat and place it in a bowl. Spoon oatmeal onto it.

5. Mix it with spinach and brie cheese. Place the egg on the top of it. Sprinkle the black pepper and salt onto it.

Nutrition (Per Serving):

Protein: 84.63 g

Calories: 7435

Carbohydrates: 71.68 g

Fat: 784.87 g

Collard And Potato Meal With Fried Egg

Preparation Time: 5 minutes

Cooking Time: 20 minutes

Servings: 2

Ingredients:

- 2 tbsp. olive oil
- 1 yellow potato,
- 1 Onion chopped
- 2 clove garlic (minced)
- 1 tsp. cumin
- 1 tsp. salt
- 1 tsp. black pepper
- 1 c. green peas (boiled)
- 2 collard green

- 2 large size eggs
- 1 boneless bowl of chicken
- 1 beefsteak tomato
- 1 bowl roasted red pepper sauce (optional)

Directions:

1. Place a frying pan on heat and put two tablespoons of oil into it. Add chopped onions, peas, and potatoes, shredded chicken, and cook until they become light fried.
2. Add black pepper, salt, cumin, and garlic into the potatoes. After this, add collard, add two cups of water, and stir it occasionally. Now remove the collard and potato mixture from the heat.
3. After this, sprinkle a few drops of olive oil in the frying pan and cook the egg on the pan. Finally, pick a bowl, place the potato mixture on the sides of the bowl, and fried eggs on the top of it.
4. Place sliced tomato around it to make it look better. Sprinkle the salt and black pepper onto it. Your delicious iron-rich meal is ready served with sprigs of thymes. Have a nice day.

Nutrition (Per Serving):

Protein: 39.59 g

Calories: 1066

Carbohydrates: 134.65 g

Fat: 44.23 g

Roasted Broccoli And Root Veggie Breakfast Tacos

Preparation Time: 10 minutes

Cook Time: 15 minutes

Servings: 2

Ingredients:

- 2 sweet potatoes (small size)
- 2 carrot (peeled and sliced)
- 2 radish (peeled and sliced)
- 2 tbsp. olive oil
- Any tomato paste
- 2 tsp. ground cumin
- 1 c. cheddar cheese
- 2 tsp. ground coriander
- 2 tsp. salt
- 2 lemons (peeled)
- 1 c. canned beans (mashed)
- 2 pita bread

Directions:

1. Pick a small bowl and add all the ingredients like potatoes, carrots, salt, oil, broccoli, and the rest of the ingredients. Mix all the ingredients thoroughly.

2. Place a frying pan on heat, adds a few drops in the pan, and fry the bread until it becomes light brown. Preheat the oven to 300°F.
3. Keep a baking sheet in the oven and place the bowl. Roast it for 20 minutes. When the vegetables and beans become ready, place the pita bread on the plate, place a tomato sauce, and put a layer of the bean.
4. Add all the roasted vegetables material and shredded cheddar cheese. Your healthy breakfast is ready. Enjoy it.

Nutrition (Per Serving):

Protein: 13.95 g

Calories: 487

Carbohydrates: 78.85 g

Fat: 16.55 g

Fried Rice With Scrambled Eggs Breakfast

Preparation Time: 30 minutes

Total Time: 1 hour

Servings: 5

Ingredients:

- 1 tbsp. ginger and garlic paste

- ½ c. vegetable oil
- 1 green onion (chopped)
- 1 tbsp. Red onion
- 1 tbsp. parsley
- 2 c. cooked brown rice
- 2 tbsp. soya sauce
- 1 green onion
- 1 c. cabbage (shredded)
- 1 c. carrot (shredded)
- 2 tbsp. Mirin
- 1 c. peas
- 2 eggs beat (large)
- 1 tbsp. sunflower seeds
- 1 tbsp. cashews (chopped)
- 3 Cucumber (Sliced)
- 1 bowl Tomato Sauce

Directions:

1. Start by putting the oil into a skillet. Add ingredients you want to fry, like garlic and ginger paste, onion peas, and cabbage.
2. Fry these ingredients in the oil until the ginger and the other vegetables are browned. Add the boiled rice continue to stir it. Add the soya sauce and Mirin as well.

3. Stir it and remove it from the heat. Place a frying pan on heat and spray a small amount of oil. Add egg and fry it until it becomes scrambled.
4. Add fried rice to the bowl or plate. Place the egg at the top of the rice. In the end, place sunflower seeds, mint leaves, and toasted cashews on the top of the egg.
5. You can place cucumber at the side of the plate. Now serve it along with tomato ketchup or tomato sauce. Your yummy breakfast is ready. Enjoy this and have a good day ahead.

Nutrition (Per Serving):

Protein: 3.96 g

Calories: 478

Carbohydrates: 12.33 g

Fat: 48.54 g

Shakes And Smoothies

Iron-Rich Spinach And Parsley Smoothie

Preparation Time: 5 minutes

Servings: 1

Ingredients:

- 1 c. parsley
- 2 c. spinach
- 1 lemon juice
- 1 c. pineapple
- 1 c. water

Directions:

1. Start by putting all the ingredients in the blender let them blend. Pour them in a glass or have fun.

Nutrition (Per Serving):

Protein: 4.85 g

Calories: 198

Carbohydrates: 48.79 g

Fat: 1.02 g

Pink Iron Boosting Smoothie

Preparation Time: 10 minutes

Servings: 2

Ingredients

- 1 beet cooked
- 1 c. raspberries
- 1 dried apricot

- 1 tsp. molasses
- 1 avocado
- 1 banana
- 1 c. oat milk

Directions:

1. Start by putting all the ingredients in the blend. Blend them well. Pour them into a glass or jar. Enjoy it and have fun.

Nutrition (Per Serving):

Protein: 25.36 g

Calories: 1193

Carbohydrates: 220.33 g

Fat: 38.83 g

Iron-Rich Tropical Green Smoothie

Preparation Time: 5 minutes

Servings: 1

Ingredients:

- 1 c. spinach
- 1 c. kale washed
- 1 orange (juice)
- 1 lemon juice

- 1 c. pineapple
- 4 oz. s water

Directions:

1. Start by putting all the ingredients in the blender. Let them blend until it becomes a pure mixture. Pour them into a jar or glass and have fun.

Nutrition (Per Serving):

Protein: 4.45 g

Calories: 297

Carbohydrates: 73.63 g

Fat: 0.88 g

Iron-Rich Strawberry Shake

Preparation Time: 10 minutes

Servings: 2

Ingredients:

- 1 c. strawberries
- 1 c. milk
- 1 c. strawberry ice-cream
- 1 tbsp. honey/sugar
- Nuts (Optional)

Directions:

1. Wash all the strawberries. Let them dry. Remove their stems and cut them into halves. Place all of these things like strawberries, milk, and ice cream into the juicer blender.
2. Add honey or sugar if you like a sweeter taste. It will depend on your choice. Blend it until unless it becomes a pure smoothie. Pour it into a glass.
3. You can add crushed nuts for the sprinkle. Serve it with a straw on a plate. Place 2 to 3 strawberries aside this glass to give it a yummy look. Your Iron-rich strawberries shake ready. Enjoy it and stay healthy.

Nutrition (Per Serving):

Protein: 9.06 g

Calories: 335

Carbohydrates: 42.52 g

Fat: 15.98 g

Iron-Boosting Orange Green Smoothie

Preparation Time: 5 minutes

Servings: 1

Ingredients:

- 1 c. spinach

- 2 bananas
- 1 orange
- 1 c. orange juice
- 1 c. yogurt
- 1 tbsp. chia seeds
- 3 ice cubes
- 3 dates

Directions:

1. Start by adding all ingredients apart from dates in a blender and blending it.
2. Add dates and mix it well.
3. Pour it into a glass or jar. Serve it and enjoy it.

Nutrition (Per Serving):

Protein: 20.29 g

Calories: 805

Carbohydrates: 148.71 g

Fat: 19.24 g

Mouthwatering Watermelon Smoothie

Preparation Time: 5 minutes

Servings: 1

Ingredients:

- 1 c. cubes of watermelon
- ½ c. strawberries
- 2 tbsp. honey
- Unsweetened almond milk or 1 c. of water
- 2 mint sprigs
- Black salt (Optional)

Directions:

1. Place strawberries, watermelon, unsweetened milk, and honey into the juicer blender. Let them blend until they become a smooth smoothie.
2. You can add water or milk if the smoothie is too thick. If you like, you can add a few pts. of black taste instead of honey or along with love. Pour it into a glass.
3. Place this glass onto a dish and add a few numbers of strawberries and mint leaves on the plate to look attractive. Serve it along with a straw and enough it immediately.

Nutrition (Per Serving):

Protein: 9.06 g

Calories: 335

Carbohydrates: 42.52 g

Fat: 15.98 g

Yummy Date Shake Recipe

Preparation Time: 5 minutes

Cook Time: 5 minutes

Servings: 1

Ingredients

- 5 dates (Seedless)
- 1c. almond milk
- ½ tbsp. cinnamon powder

Directions:

1. Wash all the seedless dates. Place it into a juicer blender. Add a c. of almond milk. Add cinnamon powder. You can add sugar or honey. It will depend on you if you like a sweeter taste.
2. Let it blend till it becomes a smoothie. Pour it into a glass. You can add crushed nuts or chopped dates to garnish it. Serve it and enjoy its taste.

Nutrition (Per Serving):

Protein: 2.54 g

Calories: 230

Carbohydrates: 52.29 g

Fat: 3.19 g

Banana And Grapefruit Smoothie

Preparation Time: 5 minutes

Cook Time: 10 minutes

Servings: 1

Ingredients

- 1 Banana
- 1 grapefruit
- 2 honey or sugar

Directions

1. Start by cutting the fruits. Put these fruits into the juicer blenders. Let them mix till they all become a smoothie.
2. Add honey according to your taste. Pour it into a glass. Enjoy this delicious smoothie and have a great day.

Nutrition (Per Serving):

Protein: 5.3 g

Calories: 568

Carbohydrates: 145.02 g

Fat: 2.06 g

Meat And Poultry

Iron-Rich Pork And Broccoli Meat

Preparation Time: 10 minutes

Cooking Time: 20 minutes

Servings: 2

Ingredients:

- ½ pound pork
- 1 c. beef broth
- 2 c. broccoli florets
- 1 carrot (sliced)
- 1 green bell pepper
- 3 spring onion
- 1 tbsp. corn flour
- 1 tbsp. olive oil
- ½ c. soya sauce
- 1 tbsp. sweetener
- 3 cloves garlic (minced)

Directions:

1. Start by placing pork into a large bowl and mixing it with corn flour. Using your hands, place corn starch on each part of the pork and set it aside.
2. Keep a frying pan on the heat until it becomes hot. Add pork into this oil until no pink color is left on its skin. Crumble the meat with hard utensils.
3. Add broccoli and carrots into the pan. Let them fry for 5-6 minutes and add more beef broth. Add green bell pepper into it too. Along with this, mix the soya sauce with the other sauce ingredients in a saucepan until it starts to simmer.
4. Put the pork and other cooked ingredients and sauce into the pan and wait for the moment until all the ingredients mix up with each other on a low flame.
5. Add fried spring onions, black pepper, and salt according to your taste. Enjoy this recipe and have a healthy day.

Nutrition (Per Serving):

Protein: 67 g

Calories: 695

Carbohydrates: 36.51 g

Fat: 31.05 g

Beef, Broccoli, And Spinach

Preparation Time: 15 minutes

Cooking Time: 15 minutes

Servings: 2

Ingredients:

- 4-5 Spinach Leaves
- 1 flank steak
- 8 oz. broccoli florets
- 2 tbsp. olive oil
- 1 tbsp. garlic (minced)
- 3 tbsp. salt and pepper
- ½ c. coconut amino sauce
- 1 tbsp. garlic powder
- 1 tbsp. onion powder
- 1 tbsp. ginger powder

Directions:

1. Start with placing the steaks pieces into a bowl. Add all the ingredients to marinate it and mix the meat fully. Let them place for at least an hour. So that steaks can absorb all the nutrients.
2. Put some olive oil in the pan and heat it on a medium flame. Add a layer of beef to the skillet.

Heat the layer of beef on a low flame until the steaks become light brownie from all sides.

3. Add the broccoli florets and the leftover marinade to the boil too. In the end, add salt and pepper. Make a topping of the green onions and enjoy it.

Nutrition (Per Serving):

Protein: 47.66 g

Calories: 518

Carbohydrates: 49.1 g

Fat: 21.73 g

Honey And Mustard Chicken Thighs With Spring Veg

Preparation Time: 10 minutes

Cooking Time: 40 minutes

Servings: 3

Ingredients:

- 1 lemon (juice and zest)
- 1 garlic clove (crushed)
- 1 tbsp. honey
- 3 chicken thigh
- 1 tbsp. mustard
- 4 potatoes
- 50 g Chinese Spinach

- 1 tbsp. olive oil
- 50 g peas
- 2 carrots (sliced)

Directions:

1. Start with placing the thigh in the bowl. Add the honey, garlic, mustard, lemon juice, and lemon zest into the same bowl to marinate it. Let it place for 1 hour so that the chicken can absorb all the nutrients from the ingredients.
2. Place this thigh on a large baking plate and fill the potatoes in the spaces. Sprinkle salt and pepper over the thigh. Bake it at 180°C until all the chicken becomes brown.
3. Following this, remove the dish from the oven. Add spinach leaves and peas on the plate and put them in the oven too.
4. When the peas become hot and spinach becomes brown, you can present it with the sauce. Enjoy this iron-rich chicken thigh recipe and enjoy the meal.

Nutrition (Per Serving):

Protein: 43.48 g

Calories: 902

Carbohydrates: 99.7 g

Fat: 37.41 g

Roast Lamb With A Vegetable Salad

Preparation Time: 10 minutes

Cooking Time: 40 minutes

Servings: 2

Ingredients:

- 1 ½-c. barley
- 1 c. sunflower oil
- 350g lamb roast
- 1 bunch carrots (scrubbed)
- 1 large red onion (wedges)
- 1 tbsp. lemon juice
- 1 tbsp. salt
- 2 large size cucumbers (sliced)
- 1 c. parsley leaves

Directions:

1. Start with placing a skillet on the heat. Place 2 c. of water in it and 1 tbsp. of salt. After this, add barley into it. Let it boil at low heat. Simmer it for 20 minutes.
2. Rinse them below the cold water. Add oil in the saucepan and fry the lamb from both sides until it browned.

3. Shift it on a roasting pan. Assemble carrots and red onions around the meat. After adding the remaining oil and salt, and pepper.
4. Roast it for 30 minutes until the lamb's skin becomes dark brown. Cover it with foil and keep it on a plate.
5. Place lemon juice and leaves of parsley on its top. Now the meat is ready. Enjoy its taste and have a healthy life.

Nutrition (Per Serving):

Protein: 61.54 g

Calories: 1943

Carbohydrates: 133.95 g

Fat: 131.86 g

Iron-Rich Chicken Skewers

Preparation Time: 10 minutes

Cook Time: 30 minutes

Servings: 1

Ingredients:

- 1 tbsp. sunflower oil
- One clove of garlic (Chopped)
- 1 tbsp. oregano

- 1 tbsp. pepper
- 1 kg chicken steak
- 1 tbsp. sea salt

Directions:

1. Start with making the chicken pc. and place them in a chicken. Add oil, oregano, and garlic. Following this, add pepper and a spoon of salt.
2. Put these pieces into skewers. Heat the barbecue plate on a medium flame and cook it from both sides until they cook.
3. Shift them on the plate. Cover with gold foil. Now they are ready to eat. Have a great day ahead.

Nutrition (Per Serving):

Protein: 204.55 g

Calories: 1261

Carbohydrates: 6.49 g

Fat: 41.18 g

Lamb Shanks With Rhubarb

Preparation Time: 10 minutes

Cooking Time: 2 hours

Servings: 2

Ingredients:

- 1 tbsp. tomato Paste
- 1 tbsp. cinnamon powder
- 1 tbsp. turmeric powder
- 1 tbsp. sunflower oil
- Two lamb shanks
- One green onion (sliced)
- One garlic clove (crushed)
- 1 tbsp. coriander powder
- Two rhubarb stalks
- 1 tbsp. saffron
- 1 c. Massel stock
- 1 tbsp. Parsley chopped leaves
- 100g packet pearl couscous

Directions:

1. Start with placing a skillet on a medium flame. Add lamb pc. and cook them until they become brown. Place it on a separate plate. Add oil into the frying pan.
2. Add garlic and onion into it and cook it for 5 minutes. Add cinnamon, saffron, coriander, and saffron.
3. Add tomato paste, stock, and one cup of water. Let it boil, place lamb again in the pan, cover it for 1 hour and 40 minutes, and let it cook.

4. Remove the dish's cover and let it cook until the meat becomes separate from the bones.
5. Add rhubarb and cook it until it becomes soft. Place it in a bowl and serve it with parsley topping. Enjoy it and have a great day.

Nutrition (Per Serving):

Protein: 116.36 g

Calories: 793

Carbohydrates: 22.78 g

Fat: 27.37 g

Beef And Pine Nut Meatballs With Parsley Salad

Preparation Time: 30 minutes

Cook Time: 60 minutes

Servings: 2

Ingredients:

- 1 c. currants
- 1 garlic clove (chopped)
- 1 green onion (chopped)
- 1 c. parsley leaves (chopped)
- ½ c. mint leaves
- 1 tsp. cinnamon powder
- ½ c. breadcrumbs

- 40g pine nuts
- 300g Beef mince
- 100g hummus
- Pita bread
- 3 sprigs of parsley (for salad)
- ½ c. mint leaves (chopped)
- 2 green onions (sliced)
- 100g cherry tomatoes
- 1 tsp. cumin powder
- 1 tbsp. lemon juice
- 1 c. olive oil

Directions:

1. Start with placing currants in a heatproof bowl and cover them with boiling water. Preheat it to 200°C.
2. Let it for 5 minutes. Add mint, garlic, onion, cinnamon breadcrumbs in a blender. Blend them until rough paste forms. Spoon it into a large bowl, add pepper and salt, and mix it well.
3. Roll this material in the form of balls. You can keep the shape according to your desire.
4. Place these balls on a tray and bake them for 30 minutes. Now place it on a plate and serve any sauce with pita bread according to your taste.

Nutrition (Per Serving):

Protein: 43.88 g

Calories: 1650

Carbohydrates: 57.17 g

Fat: 143.47 g

Crusted Chicken With Sweet Roasted Vegetables

Preparation Time: 15 minutes

Cooking Time: 30 minutes

Servings: 2

Ingredients:

- 250g small-sized potatoes (halved)
- 1 bunch spring onion (halved)
- 1 tbsp. sunflower oil
- 1 tbsp. maple syrup
- 1 c. cracker crumbs
- 1 of Fresh chives (chopped)
- 1kg chicken roast
- 1 tbsp. regular Dijon mustard
- 1 tbsp. Bisto gravy powder
- 1 c. water
- 4 sprigs of spinach

Directions:

1. Start with placing the onion radish in a roasting pan. Add maple syrup and oil in a bowl and drizzle over vegetables. Remember to pre-heat the oven to 220°C and roast it for 15 minutes.
2. Along with this, add chives and breadcrumbs in a bowl. Sprinkle with salt and pepper. Place a frying pan over medium heat and put oil in it.
3. Heat the oil in it and fry the chicken until it becomes brown. Place it on the chopping board. Place Dijon mustard all over the chicken.
4. Place breadcrumbs over the chicken and coat with it. Add chicken with all other vegetables in a frying pan and roast for 25 minutes until you want it to be cooked.
5. In the end, place gravy powder in a heatproof jug and add boiled water into it. Stir it until it becomes smooth. Slice the remaining chicken and serve with spinach, roasted vegetables, and gravy.

Nutrition (Per Serving):

Protein: 105.56 g

Calories: 763

Carbohydrates: 31.6 g

Fat: 21.57 g

Dessert

Delicious Iron-Rich Chocolate Bites

Preparation Time: 10 minutes

Cooking Time: 5 minutes

Servings: 5

Ingredients:

- 1 c. almonds
- 1 c. apricots
- 1 c. cashews
- 1 oz. dark chocolate chips
- 1 c. coconut (shredded)
- 1 c. pistachios
- 1 c. dates (shredded)
- 1 pinch of salt to taste

Directions:

1. Start with placing the apricots and dates in the bowl, add some water and let it soak for 10 minutes. After that, let it dry for a few minutes.
2. Put this apricot and dates into a blender and let it blend until it becomes a fine mixture. Add cashews,

almonds, pistachios, chocolate chips, and a salt pinch.

3. Let the processor blend it. After a while when it becomes a blended material. Keep it on a separate dish and make small balls.
4. You can use any cookie shaper to give it a shape. Roll it into the coconut powder. You can enjoy it instantly or freeze it for months to enjoy it later.

Nutrition (Per Serving):

Protein: 67.17 g

Calories: 3178

Carbohydrates: 330.47 g

Fat: 201.71 g

Iron-Rich Choco Bites

Preparation Time: 15 minutes

Cooking Time: 20 minutes

Servings: 1

Ingredients:

- 2 tbsp. Molasses
- ½ c. Sesame seeds
- ½ c. Almonds
- ½ c. cashews

- ½ c. dried apricots
- ½ c. dates
- ½ c. dark chocolate
- ½ c. chia seeds
- 1 c. oats
- Coconut for garnishing

Directions:

1. Start with placing molasses, apricots, and dates into a blender. Let them blend for a few minutes. After this, add the other ingredients and again blend it until it becomes a smooth mixture.
2. Make balls of the ingredients with the help of your hands. Place oats and coconut powder on a plate and roll your balls into this material.
3. Your Iron-rich Choco bites are ready. You can enjoy it on the spot and keep it in the refrigerator to enjoy it later.

Nutrition (Per Serving):

Protein: 90.33 g

Calories: 3630

Carbohydrates: 332.69 g

Fat: 256.66 g

Banana Pops With Cocoa Powder

Preparation Time: 15 minutes

Cooking Time: 2 hours 15 minutes

Servings: 2

Ingredients:

- 2 bananas
- 4 popsicle sticks
- 2 tbsp. coconut powder
- 1 tbsp. coconut oil
- 1 c. chocolate chips
- 2 tbsp. sprinkles
- 1 c. whipped cream
- 6 cherries

Directions:

1. Start with placing a baking sheet on a tray and cutting the bananas into halves. Enter this banana in each Popsicle stick. Let them freeze.
2. Pick a bowl and add chocolate chips and coconut oil in a microwave. Stir it completely until it becomes melted. Put sprinkles in a separate bowl.
3. Remove the bananas sticks from the refrigerator and top them in melted chocolate chips.

4. Add sprinkles over it and place them on a baking sheet and keep them in the refrigerator to freeze them. Serve it with a topping of cherry, cocoa powder, and whipped cream.

Nutrition (Per Serving):

Protein: 12.95 g

Calories: 1300

Carbohydrates: 132.35 g

Fat: 87 g

Yummy Peach Crisp

Preparation Time: 15 minutes

Cooking Time: 1 hour 15 minutes

Servings: 3

Ingredients:

- 3 peaches (sliced)
- 2 tbsp. granulated sugar
- 1 tbsp. lemon juice
- 1 tbsp. cinnamon powder
- 1 c. all-purpose flour
- 1 tbsp. brown sugar
- ½ salt
- 2 pc. butter (cubes)

- 2 tbsp. oats

Directions:

1. Preheat the oven to 350°C. Pick a large skillet and add peaches, cinnamon powder, lemon juice, and sugar. Place this skillet on a baking dish, pick a bowl, and mix the flour, sugar, and salt.
2. Add butter into this bowl and mix it. After this, add oats and mix them with your hands.
3. Now add this mixture to the topping of the peaches and bake them until they become cooked. Now, they are ready to enjoy this yummy dessert and have fun.

Nutrition (Per Serving):

Protein: 15.83 g

Calories: 996

Carbohydrates: 131.77 g

Fat: 48.18 g

Chocolate Covered Watermelon

Preparation Time: 10 minutes

Cooking Time: 1 hour and 10 minutes

Servings: 4

Ingredients:

- 1 watermelon
- 1tbsp. coconut oil
- 1 tbsp. Kosher salt

Directions:

1. Start with placing a baking sheet. Now place watermelon slices over it and let them freeze for an hour. Put the coconut oil into chocolate. Mix them well.
2. Remove the watermelon from the refrigerator and dip them one by one in the chocolate mixture. Sprinkle kosher salt.
3. Let them freeze again. Now it is ready to serve. Enjoy it and have fun.

Nutrition (Per Serving):

Protein: 0.07 g

Calories: 121

Carbohydrates: 0.92 g

Fat: 13.62 g

Cheesecake-Stuffed Strawberries

Preparation Time: 20 minutes

Servings: 3

Ingredients:

- 1 cream cheese
- 1 tbsp. powdered sugar
- 1 c. heavy cream
- 15 strawberries (hollowed out)
- Crushed Almond crackers

Directions:

1. Start with beating the cream cheese for 2 to 3 minutes. Add heavy cream and powdered sugar and beat it.
2. Put this mixture into a piping bag and place it on the strawberries you like to add.
3. Now garnish it with almond crackers. Serve it and have fun.

Nutrition (Per Serving):

Protein: 5.94 g

Calories: 593

Carbohydrates: 26.41 g

Fat: 53.66 g

Banana Split Kebabs

Preparation Time: 15 minutes

Servings: 4

Ingredients:

- 4 bananas pc.
- 5 pc. pineapples
- 10 skewers
- 20 strawberries
- 1 c. chocolate chips
- 1 c. Peanuts chopped

Directions:

1. Start with entering each of the fruit slices into skewers. Assemble the fruit slices in each skewer.
2. Place the chocolate chips in the microwave and melt them. Now spread these melted chocolate chips on over the fruit skewers.
3. Freeze it and have fun.

Nutrition (Per Serving):

Protein: 83.37 g

Calories: 2277

Carbohydrates: 281.23 g

Fat: 108.73 g

Iron-Rich Sesame Candy

Preparation Time: 15 minutes

Cooking Time: 10 minutes

Servings: 2

Ingredients:

- 1 c. sesame seeds
- 1 c. brown sugar
- 1 c. water
- 1 tsp. peanut oil

Directions:

1. Start with roasting the sesame seeds in a pan. Let them be golden. Place the saucepan on heat, add brown sugar, and mix completely.
2. Pour the mixture with the help of a filter. Heat it till it reaches a stage where it becomes hard.
3. When it reaches the desired stage, turn off the heat. Now add sesame seeds and mix them. Let the mixture cool down and grease your fingers with sunflower oil and make balls of these ingredients.
4. Wait for the balls to cool down. Now they are ready to eat.

Nutrition (Per Serving):

Protein: 30.94 g

Calories: 1822

Carbohydrates: 233.39 g

Fat: 96.32 g

Vegan And Vegetarian

Easy Chickpea Coconut Milk Curry With Kale

Preparation Time: 20 minutes

Cooking Time: 30 minutes

Servings: 6

Ingredients:

- 1 lb. kale (diced)
- 2 tbsp. avocado oil
- 1 medium green onion (diced)
- 2 cloves garlic (peeled)
- 1 tbsp. ginger (peeled)
- 1tbsp. turmeric (peeled)
- 1 c. cooked chickpeas
- 200ml coconut milk
- 1 c. water
- 1 tsp. salt
- 1 tbsp. curry powder
- 1 tbsp. turmeric powder
- 1 tbsp. cumin powder
- 2 tsp. garam masala

- 1 ½ lime (juice)

Directions:

1. Start with placing a skillet on the heat and pour oil into it. Add ginger, garlic, onion, and Kale. Now cook it until the onion becomes brown.
2. After this, adds Kale into it until its color becomes changed and add chickpeas. Stir it and add pepper and salt.
3. Add turmeric, curry powder, garam masala, and cumin. Stir it continuously and add coconut milk, salt, and water.
4. Add curry into it until its flavors blend. Turn off heat add lime juice, salt, and pepper according to your taste.
5. Serve it and have a nice day.

Nutrition (Per Serving):

Protein: 21.25 g

Calories: 1372

Carbohydrates: 56.73 g

Fat: 129.14 g

Chard And Lentil Stuffed Sweet Potato

Preparation Time: 10 minutes

Cook Time: 45 minutes

Servings: 1

Ingredients:

- 4 florets of Chard
- 4 sweet potatoes
- 2 cloves garlic (minced)
- 1 c. dried lentils
- 1 tsp. olive oil
- 2 tbsp. mint leaves (chopped)
- 1 tbsp. black pepper
- 1 tbsp. Salt
- 1 c. water
- 1 tbsp. plain Greek yogurt

Directions:

1. Before moving forward, preheat the oven to 300°F. Wash the sweet potatoes and wrap each potato in foil. Bake each foil for about 40 minutes.
2. Remove the sweet potatoes from the oven and keep them wrapped until ready to serve. Place a saucepan on the heat, add water and lentils, and let it boil. Let it boil until the lentils absorb all the water.

3. Along with this, heat oil in a skillet on the heat. Add chard and garlic. Stir it occasionally. Add lentils and stir.
4. After that, remove it from heat, divide sweet potatoes into two halves, and place them on the plate. Fill the centers of the sweet potatoes with chard and lentils.
5. Make a topping of the yogurt and mint leaves, and black pepper. Your chard and sweet potato recipes are ready. Eat it and have a great day.

Nutrition (Per Serving):

Protein: 17.55 g

Calories: 334

Carbohydrates: 44.6 g

Fat: 15.09 g

Iron-Rich Veggie Beetroot Curry

Preparation Time: 15 minutes

Cooking Time: 10 minutes

Servings: 3

Ingredients:

- 4 c. red beetroot
- 2 tbsp. olive oil

- 1 tbsp. black pepper
- 1 tbsp. ginger & garlic paste
- 1 tbsp. sunflower seeds
- 1 green bell pepper (chopped)
- 1 red bell pepper (chopped)
- 1 yellow bell pepper (chopped)
- 1 c. carrots (chopped)
- 1 c. baby corn (chopped)
- 1 tbsp. salt and black pepper
- 1 c. spinach leaves
- 1 tbsp. soya sauce
- 1 tbsp. vinegar
- 1 c. water
- 3 oz. tofu

Directions:

1. Start by putting the pan on the heat adds oil into it. Add ginger, garlic paste, sunflower seeds, and stir it occasionally when the oil becomes hot.
2. Once you feel the garlic and ginger paste fragment, you can add the rest of the vegetables and fry them well so that they all cook well and prove a healthy meal for you.
3. After this, place them in a bowl and sprinkle salt and black pepper on them. Place 4 to 5 mint leaves

to make it look yummy. Your Iron rich meal is ready to enjoy and have fun.

Nutrition (Per Serving):

Protein: 15.73 g

Calories: 738

Carbohydrates: 136.22 g

Fat: 19.61 g

Yellow Dal With Millet

Preparation Time: 15 minutes

Cook Time: 45 minutes

Servings: 1

Ingredients:

- 2 c. cooked millet
- 1 tsp. cumin powder
- 1 tsp. coriander powder
- 1 c. yellow split peas
- 1 medium onion
- 1 tsp. ginger & garlic paste
- 1 tsp. turmeric powder
- 1 tsp. salt
- 1 c. chopped green bell pepper
- 1 c. chopped red bell pepper

- 2 tbsp. basil (chopped)

Directions:

1. Start with washing the yellow split peas. Place a skillet on the heat and put four cups of water in it. Add onion pieces, spices, salt, and ginger into it.
2. Let it boil and stir it occasionally. Cook it for 40 min till the peas become tender. After this, turn off the heat, pick a blender, and add all the ingredients to make a pureed mixture.
3. Add fried bell peppers. Sprinkle a spoon of salt and serve it with cooked millet.

Nutrition (Per Serving):

Protein: 25.84 g

Calories: 694

Carbohydrates: 134.54 g

Fat: 6.71 g

Crispy Baked Tofu Paneer With Spicy Garlic Sauce

Preparation Time: 30 minutes

Cooking Time: 30 minutes

Servings: 1

Ingredients:

- 10-oz. tofu
- 1 c. arrowroot
- 2 tbsp. pepper cracked
- 1 c. breadcrumbs
- 1 tsp. salt
- 1 c. almond milk
- 1c. nutritional yeast
- 1 tbsp. grounded garlic
- 1 tbsp. graham masala
- Spicy Garlic Sauce

Directions:

1. Preheat the oven to 400°F. Place baking sheet along with parchment. Place 3 bowls for the breading of the tofu. Add salt, pepper, and arrowroot to the first bowl.
2. In the second bowl assemble, pepper, yeast, salt, graham masala, and garlic powder. In the third bowl, add milk. Cut the tofu into two halves and place 8 triangles of it.
3. Mix the tofu in the arrowroot mixture, almond milk, and bread crumb mixture. Lay down on the baking sheet. Bake it so that both sides become crispy.
4. Remove from oven and serve with a bowl of spicy garlic sauce.

Nutrition (Per Serving):

Protein: 130.91 g

Calories: 1716

Carbohydrates: 167.65 g

Fat: 66.95 g

Swiss Chard And White Bean Casserole

Preparation Time: 30 minutes

Cooking Time: 1 hour

Servings: 2

Ingredients:

- 1 small green onion (chopped)
- 2 tbsp. olive oil
- 1 bunch chard
- 1 tbsp. all-purpose flour
- 1 c. oat milk
- 2 tbsp. yeast
- 1 clove garlic (crushed)
- 1 sweet potato
- 12 oz. cannellini
- 1 c. almond parmesan
- 1 nutmeg
- 1 tbsp. salt and pepper

Directions:

1. Start with preheating the oven to 300°C. Place skillet on the heat. Heat the oil in the skillet and add onion until they become fried.
2. Add chard and a pinch of salt and cook until it becomes moisture-free. Place them in a separate bowl.
3. Add remaining oil and flour into it and mix them well. After this, add oat milk and blend it. Add yeast and garlic into it and let it boil.
4. Remove it from the heat and add salt and pepper to it. Oil a dish and lay the sweet potatoes slightly in a layer. Next, spread ½ of the beans and ½ of the sauce.
5. Repeat this pattern and top with parmesan. Cover it with foil and bake for 50 minutes. Now enjoy it and have fun.

Nutrition (Per Serving):

Protein: 16.25 g

Calories: 590

Carbohydrates: 56.24 g

Fat: 38.18 g

Vegan Apple Pie Oatmeal

Preparation Time: 5 minutes

Cooking Time: 15 minutes

Servings: 1

Ingredients:

- 1 c. water
- 1 c. quick oats
- 1 tbsp. hemp hearts
- 1 tbsp. tahini
- 2 pinch salt
- 2 small apples (chopped)
- 1 tbsp. maple syrup
- 1 tbsp. coconut oil
- 1 tbsp. tahini
- 1 tsp. vanilla extract

Directions:

1. Start with boiling the water in a small skillet, add salt and oats and cook them on medium heat. Cover it with a lid and simmer it until the oats become cooked.
2. Alongside this, heat butter in another pan and add apples to it and steam it. Add tahini, maple syrup to a bowl. Add this sauce into the apples and stir it.

3. Remove it from the heat. When the oatmeal is ready, add hemp hearts. Place them in the bowl and serve them with chopped nuts. Have fun.

Nutrition (Per Serving):

Protein: 16.77 g

Calories: 824

Carbohydrates: 116.71 g

Fat: 35.59 g

Snacks

Apricot-Sesame Spice Bliss Balls

Preparation Time: 30 minutes

Cooking Time: 30 minutes

Servings: 1

Ingredients:

- 75g Almonds
- 75g Apricots
- 50g muesli
- 1 tbsp. maple syrup
- 1 tsp. cinnamon powder

- 1 tbsp. sesame seeds

Directions:

1. Start with putting almonds into the blender and blend them until they are finely chopped. Add honey cinnamon powder and apricots.
2. Mix them well. Place sesame seeds on the plate. Now make balls of the ingredients and coat them with sesame seeds.
3. Let them place in the refrigerator.

Nutrition (Per Serving):

Protein: 18.01 g

Calories: 605

Carbohydrates: 48.71 g

Fat: 42.45 g

Zucchini, Pumpkin, And Corn Muffins

Preparation Time: 15 minutes

Cooking Time: 25 minutes

Servings: 6

Ingredients:

- 1 c. whole meal flour
- 60g butter (chopped)

- 1 courgette (grated)
- 1 c. pumpkin (grated)
- 1 c. kernels
- 60g cheddar
- 1 egg
- 100 ml oat milk

Directions:

1. Firstly, preheat the oven to 150 and Greece the muffin pan with oil. Place flour in a large bowl.
2. Now add butter and Courgette and cheddar. Whisk the milk and egg in a bowl.
3. Add to the flour mixture and stir it until it becomes combined. Bake for 30 mins. Now enjoy it and have fun.

Nutrition (Per Serving):

Protein: 18.87 g

Calories: 399

Carbohydrates: 12.52 g

Fat: 32.57 g

Apple Doughnuts

Preparation Time: 10 minutes

Cooking Time: 12 min

Servings: 6

Ingredients:

- 1 apple
- 140g fruit yogurt
- 1 c. strawberries (chopped)
- 1 bowl Toasted muesli
- 1 orange (chopped)
- 2 bananas (crushed)
- 5 kiwi fruit (chopped)
- 1 bowl grapes

Directions:

1. Start with cutting each apple into slices. To make strawberries sweeter donuts, spoon them over yogurt.
2. Sprinkle them with strawberries. To make kiwi fruit, spoon over yogurt and sprinkle kiwi fruits. Now serve apple donuts immediately.

Nutrition (Per Serving):

Protein: 6.55 g

Calories: 322

Carbohydrates: 54.87 g

Fat: 11.29 g

Cranberry And Oat Balls

Preparation Time: 30 minutes

Cooking Time: 50 minutes

Servings: 10

Ingredients:

- 10 dates (chopped)
- 45goats
- 20g dried cranberries
- 25g pumpkin seeds
- 1 tbsp. almond butter

Directions:

1. Firstly, place the dates in a blender and blend them until it becomes a pure smoothie.
2. Add oats, pepitas, almond butter, and cranberries. Mix them well. Place a baking paper in a baking tray.
3. By using your hands, make balls of the mixture. Place them on the tray.

Nutrition (Per Serving):

Protein: 7.1 g

Calories: 76

Carbohydrates: 6.27 g

Fat: 2.8 g

Iron-Rich Nuts Snack Mix

Preparation Time: 15 minutes

Cooking Time: 15 minutes

Servings: 2

Ingredients:

- 2 c. Cheerios cereal
- 1 c. cashews (unsalted)
- 1 c. almonds (unsalted)
- 1 c. walnuts
- 1 c. peanuts (unsalted)
- 1 c. cherries (dried)
- 1 tsp. turmeric powder
- 1 tsp. cumin powder
- 1 c. pretzels
- 1 c. sunflower oil
- 1 tsp. paprika (smoked)
- 1 tsp. Salt.

Directions:

1. Start with mixing all the ingredients like nuts, cherries, pretzels, etc., and add the sunflower oil. Add spices and salt to the bowl and mix them well.

2. Preheat the oven to 315 F. Place a baking sheet with parchment paper and keep it aside. After mixing it, place it on a parchment sheet and paper.
3. Keep it in the oven and bake it. Your yummy iron-rich snacks are ready. Serve it and have fun.

Nutrition (Per Serving):

Protein: 68.56 g

Calories: 3112

Carbohydrates: 169.14 g

Fat: 256.44 g

Almond Crunch Clusters Snacks

Preparation Time: 10 minutes

Cooking Time: 30 minutes

Servings: 2

Ingredients:

- 1 tbsp. Black Treacle
- 1 tbsp. Peanut Butter
- 1 tbsp. maple syrup
- 1 tsp. cinnamon powder
- 1 c. almond slices
- 1 pinch salt
- 1 c. whole-grain cereal

- 1 tsp. vanilla extract

Directions:

1. Start with placing black treacle, peanut butter, maple syrup, cinnamon, salt, whole grain cereals, and almond slices and stir it regularly. Heat the oven to 240°F, place a baking sheet, and add parchment paper.
2. Place this mixture on a baking sheet with the help of a spoon spread it nicely. Bake it for 35 minutes.
3. Remove the dish from the oven. Let it cool and make clusters of whole-grain cereals.
4. Your Yummy and crispy iron-rich snacks are ready. Serve it or enjoy it.

Nutrition (Per Serving):

Protein: 8.12 g

Calories: 340

Carbohydrates: 67.79 g

Fat: 5.19 g

Mini Pita Pizzas

Preparation Time: 10 minutes

Cooking Time: 30 minutes

Servings: 1

Ingredients:

- 2 pita bread
- 60 g tomato pasta sauce
- 2 Tomatoes
- 1 onion chopped
- 2 tbsp. thyme herbs
- 75 g chargrilled red bell pepper
- 50 g feta cheese
- 1 tbsp. olive oil
- 5 mint leaves

Directions:

1. Preheat the oven to 250°C. Place the pita bread on a tray. Place pizza sauce on the base of every pc. of bread with the help of a spoon.
2. Place tomato and onion slices on every pita bread and thyme herb. Place bell pepper and feta cheese.
3. After this, add black pepper and salt. Add olives and mint leaves to it. Finally, bake it for 15 minutes until it becomes brown.

Nutrition (Per Serving):

Protein: 21.87 g

Calories: 648

Carbohydrates: 84.09 g

Fat: 27.3 g

Seafood And Fish

Iron-Rich Catalan Fish Stew "Zarzuela"

Preparation Time: 20 minutes

Cooking Time: 60 minutes

Servings: 2

Ingredients:

- 150 g squid
- 4 shrimp
- 250g clams
- 4 crawfish
- 250g mussels
- 200g monkfish
- 150g hake
- 60 ml sunflower oil
- 1 tbsp. salt
- 1 tbsp. black pepper
- 15g hazelnuts
- 1 clove garlic (roasted)
- 5g parsley
- 70g cherry tomatoes (roasted)

- 3g paprika
- 15g fried bread

Directions:

1. Start with placing the skillet on the heat. Add olive oil and squid. Stir it. After this, smear tomatoes with olive oil. Roast the garlic and tomatoes by placing them in the oven at 200°C.
2. Add crawfish and shrimp. Alongside this, prepare the sauce by crushing the hazelnut, parsley, garlic with tomatoes in a mortar or blender and adding black pepper and paprika.
3. After this, add water and squid to cover the fish. Fry the fish in sunflower oil and add flour. Add mussels and clams. When the mussels become open, add fish into it.
4. Stir it occasionally, and when it looks dry, add water into it. In the end, simmer it until the fish is cooked.

Nutrition (Per Serving):

Protein: 243.42 g

Calories: 1414

Carbohydrates: 36.59 g

Fat: 28.23 g

Steamed Clams With Chicken Broth Cube

Preparation Time: 20 minutes

Cooking Time: 60 minutes

Servings: 1

Ingredients:

- 2 tbsp. butter
- 1 tbsp. garlic paste
- 1 pound clams
- 2 c. water
- 1 tbsp. ginger paste
- 1 c. green onion (chopped)
- 1 chicken broth cube
- 2 lemon juice
- 1 c. cream
- 1 c. mint leaves

Directions:

1. Start with placing a frying pan over the heat. Add butter and let it melt. Add chopped onion and garlic ginger paste. Stir it occasionally till it becomes lightly browned.
2. Add cockles and cook them. Add water and chicken broth cubes. Let it boil until the clams become open and stir it occasionally.

3. Now remove it from the heat, mix lemon juice, cream and butter and stir it occasionally.
4. Place mint leaves over it. Now your iron-rich seafood is ready. Serve it along with pita bread.

Nutrition (Per Serving):

Protein: 13.8 g

Calories: 970

Carbohydrates: 75.91 g

Fat: 71.45 g

Classic Garlic Oysters With Parmesan Cheese

Preparation Time: 20 minutes

Cooking Time: 15 minutes

Servings: 1

Ingredients:

- 1 tbsp. garlic paste
- 1 tbsp. ginger paste
- 6 fresh oyster
- 2 oz. s butter
- 1 tbsp. mint leaves
- 1 tbsp. black pepper
- 1 tbsp. salt
- 1 tbsp. onion (chopped)

- 1 tbsp. parmesan cheese grated

Directions:

1. Start with placing the saucepan on the heat and adding butter to it. Let it melt for a while and add garlic and ginger paste. Remove it from heat and add all the ingredients except parmesan cheese.
2. Add garlic butter to a bowl and refrigerate it until it becomes semi-solid and mix it occasionally. Wash the oysters so that the dirt becomes removed from them.
3. Remove any open oysters as they are not healthy to eat. Pick a screwdriver and wash it fully. Place the oyster into your hand.
4. Insert the screwdriver's tip into the hinge at the back and rotate it to open the oyster. Use a knife, remove the muscles, and release the oyster from the shell.
5. Place them on a dish and plate and fill them with garlic and butter paste. Add a small amount of garlic butter and add parmesan cheese over it.
6. After placing the oysters on a baking sheet, place them in the oven. Your iron-rich seafood is ready. Serve it with mint leaves and have a good day.

Nutrition (Per Serving):

Protein: 6.79 g

Calories: 499

Carbohydrates: 11.87 g

Fat: 48.89 g

Scallops With Lemon Butter Taste

Preparation Time: 5 minutes

Cooking Time: 10 minutes

Servings: 1

Ingredients:

- 0.5-pound scallops
- 1 tbsp. butter
- 1 tbsp. salt
- 1 tbsp. black pepper
- 1 tbsp. unsalted butter
- 1 garlic minced
- 1 lemon juice
- 1 tbsp. parsley leaves

Directions:

1. Start with placing a skillet over the heat, adding butter, and letting it melt. Remove the muscles from the scallop and wash it with cold water and let it dry.

2. Place salt and black pepper into it. Put the scallop in a skillet and cook until it becomes brown. Place them aside.
3. For the lemon sauce, pick a skillet and add 1 spoon of butter in the skillet. Let it melt, and add garlic paste. Cooked it until it became brown. Add lemon juice and stir it.
4. Add salt and pepper. Now the lemon butter sauce is ready. Serve it along with scallops. Garnish it with parsley leaves and have fun.

Nutrition (Per Serving):

Protein: 29.11 g

Calories: 362

Carbohydrates: 16.11 g

Fat: 20.73 g

Mackerel With Cherry Tomatoes

Preparation Time: 15 minutes

Cooking Time: 45 minutes

Servings: 2

Ingredients:

- 2 tbsp. sunflower oil
- 1 green onion chopped

- 50g nduja
- 2 cloves garlic (chopped)
- 200g cherry tomatoes
- 200g chickpeas
- 1 lemon zest
- 2 mackerel fillets
- 1 tbsp. paprika
- 1 tbsp. parsley leaves

Directions:

1. Start with placing a frying pan on the heat. Add oil along with chopped onion and salt into it. Add nduja and cook it until it starts becoming crispy.
2. Add garlic and ginger paste into and fry it. Add tomatoes and chickpeas and cook it until it becomes soft.
3. Place lemon zest, lemon juice, and oil into it and mix well. Place the mackerel fillets on a dish and add black peppers and oil on both sides of the fillets.
4. Following this, heat a frying pan and heat the fillets on both sides. Place the chickpeas into a bowl. Place mackerel fillet on the top. In the end, place parsley leaves. Serve it enjoy this.

Nutrition (Per Serving):

Protein: 103 g

Calories: 1010

Carbohydrates: 85.6 g

Fat: 28.85 g

Baked Haddock With Melted Butter

Preparation Time: 5 minutes

Cooking Time: 15 minutes

Servings: 2

Ingredients:

- 1 lb. haddock
- 3 tbsp. melted butter
- 1 tbsp. salt
- 1 tbsp. black pepper
- 1 lemon zest
- 1 c. parsley
- 1 c. breadcrumbs (plain)

Directions:

1. Start by putting melted butter on a baking sheet, coating the bottom, and combining the breadcrumbs with the rest of the melted butter. Preheat the oven to 300°C.

2. Coat both sides of the fish with salt and pepper and place them in a baking dish. After this, place breadcrumbs over the fish as a topping.
3. Now, bake it for 20 minutes until the fish cook completely. Serve with lemon juice or place parsley leaves on the top of it. Now enjoy this delicious iron-rich fish.

Nutrition (Per Serving):

Protein: 64.73 g

Calories: 1113

Carbohydrates: 29.3 g

Fat: 88.08 g

Sardines With Chili And Lemon

Preparation Time: 25 minutes

Cooking Time: 6 minutes

Servings: 2

Ingredients:

- 1 tbsp. sunflower oil
- 1 lemon (zest)
- 1 lemon (juice)
- 1 red chili (chopped)
- 1 clove garlic

- 10 oz. sardines
- Mixed salad
- 4 drops Tabasco

Directions:

1. Start by picking a bowl and mixing the lemon juice, chili, oil, lemon zest, salt, and black pepper. Make small slices of sardine and place lemon and oil mixture on the sardines and rub it well on the surface.
2. Heat the barbecue pan and cook sardines on a preheated barbecue. Cooked both sides of the sardines. At the end of the cooking, place lemon slices near the fish before removing them from the heat.
3. Now your delicious food is ready. Serve it with a few drops of Tabasco, lemon slices, and salad.

Nutrition (Per Serving):

Protein: 37.08 g

Calories: 1136

Carbohydrates: 8.82 g

Fat: 105.8 g

Conclusion

Finally, after going through the previous chapters, it is concluded that our bodies need a balanced diet to live a healthy life. Health is the most important thing that we should care about as it is a saying that a healthy body has a healthy mind.

You need to seek treatment if you find any risk factors and symptoms associated with = anemia like constant fatigue, palpitations, pale color of your skin, and breathlessness. As mentioned before, you may become anemic if your food intake lacks vitamins and minerals or if you have a high blood flow during menstruation. If you are a pregnant woman, it could be due to the lack of supplements, especially folate.

Now you have an idea about the anemia, the types of anemia, the causes, and the symptoms. The best food for an anemic person fills the body with iron. By reading this information-packed book, you now have learned many recipes to get healthy food and live a better life.

Frequently Asked Questions

Hopefully, after reading this book, you understand a bit more about what anemia is and what causes it. There are many things to know about this disease, however, and sometimes you just need a simple answer to a simple question.

Rather than flipping through the whole book, check this list of frequently asked questions. Here you will find some of the most commonly asked questions as well as the answers about anemia.

Q: How many types of anemia are there?

A: Anemia occurs when your blood isn't able to carry enough oxygen throughout your body. This may occur due to a variety of reasons, which means there are many types of anemia. The various types of anemia are differentiated by their cause.

Q: What are the signs of anemia?

A: It takes time for anemia to develop so the symptoms may not appear suddenly. Some of the most common signs of anemia to watch out for, however, include fatigue, weakness, headache, pale skin, irregular heartbeat, shortness of breath and chest pain. Remember, signs and symptoms may vary depending on the type of anemia you have.

Q: How do I know if I have it?

A: Because many of the symptoms of anemia can be found in relation to other diseases it is not wise to diagnose yourself – you could end up missing something very serious. The best way to find out if you have anemia is to visit your doctor and to have him perform the necessary tests.

Q: What tests will my doctor perform?

A: The most important test your doctor will perform is called a complete blood count – a CBC. If the results of this test suggest that you may have anemia, you might have to take additional tests including hemoglobin electrophoresis, a reticulocyte count and iron levels.

Q: Why is a medical history important?

A: Taking a proper medical history is one of the most important aspects of a doctor's exam. A patient's history will reveal hereditary health conditions and could also point out dietary or lifestyle factors that have an impact on your risk for anemia.

Q: Why can't my doctor just prescribe me a medicine over the phone?

A: Treatments for anemia vary depending on the type and the cause – one treatment doesn't work for all types of anemia so your doctor will have to actually see you in order to make a diagnosis. Only once you have a confirmed diagnosis can your doctor prescribe the proper treatment for your condition.

Q: What are my treatment options?

A: The goal of anemia treatment is to increase the ability of your blood to carry oxygen – this involves increasing red blood cell and/or hemoglobin levels. Anemia treatment may also involve treating the underlying cause of the condition.

Q: Will it go away?

A: In many cases, anemia goes undiagnosed, and thus untreated, for far longer than it should. If not treated properly, long-term anemia can lead to organ damage and even heart failure. Even if your symptoms are mild, it could still be causing damage so you should be seen by a doctor as soon as possible.

Q: How can I prevent anemia?

A: Because there are so many different types of anemia, each with a unique cause, you may not be able to prevent every single kind. There are certain types, however, that can be prevented through dietary or lifestyle choices. Eating iron-rich foods, for example, may help to prevent certain types of anemia – taking iron supplements may help as well (particularly with iron-deficiency anemia).

Q: How much iron should I be getting every day?

A: The amount of iron you need on a daily basis varies depending on your age and sex. Developing children and pregnant/lactating women have higher needs to iron, as do young women of child-bearing age.

Q: How does birth control affect my anemia risk?

A: Many oral contraceptives help to reduce the severity of menstrual bleeding. If you typically have heavy periods, this may help to lower your blood loss and thus reduce your risk for some types of anemia.

Q: Are vegetarians more at risk for anemia?

A: Most food sources with the highest levels of iron are animal-based, largely red meat and organ meats. If you are vegetarian, you can still get iron from leafy green vegetables, beans and certain grains but you may need to be a little more conscientious about your food choices.

Q: Is it possible to get too much iron?

A: Though uncommon, iron toxicity is possible. Too much iron in the body can lead to organ damage, arthritis, missed periods, heart problems and more. If you follow a healthy diet, you shouldn't have to worry about getting too much iron.

Children, on the other hand, are more at risk for iron toxicity, though largely in cases of over-supplementation.

Q: When should I see a doctor?

A: The symptoms of anemia manifest at different times and at different severities for every individual. You know your body best so only you can decide when something has changed to the point that you need to see a doctor. If you are experiencing fatigue for unexplained reasons, you may want to ask your doctor about anemia. If, when donating blood, you are told that you have low hemoglobin levels you should also see a doctor.

Index

A

B

C

D

E

F

G

H

I

J

L

M

N

O

P

R

S

T

V

W

Photo Credits

Page 3, maroke via Canva.com (Canva Pro License)

https://www.canva.com/photos/MADVZ7FaJlg-woman-anemia-image/

Page 13, Nataliia Mysak via Canva.com (Canva Pro License)

https://www.canva.com/photos/MADUZE7lXVY-food-containing-natural-iron-fe-liver-avocado-broccoli-spinach-parsley-beans-nuts-on-a-blue-background-top-view-/

Page 25, Hailshadow via Canva.com (Canva Pro License)

https://www.canva.com/photos/MAEE0j9OHbI-iron-deficiency/

Page 49, wildpixel via Canva.com (Canva Pro License)

https://www.canva.com/photos/MADR_b16H-U-sickle-cell-cardiovascular/

Page 74, Elnur via Canva.com (Canva Pro License)

https://www.canva.com/photos/MACu2tXyDEA-patient-getting-blood-transfusion-in-hospital-clinic/

Page 94, vadimguzhva via Canva.com (Canva Pro License)

https://www.canva.com/photos/MADAirFcbtM-pregnancy/

Page 116, bit245 via Canva.com (Canva Pro License)

https://www.canva.com/photos/MADLsNy2HD4-seasonal-vegetarian-vegan-cooking-ingredients/

Page 123, bit245 via Canva.com (Canva Pro License)

https://www.canva.com/photos/MADrwvP0w4Q-foods-high-in-iron/

Page 137, Motortion via Canva.com (Canva Pro License)

https://www.canva.com/photos/MAC_JX2GMVI-attractive-woman-using-massaging-ball-muscles-relaxation-blood-circulation/

References

American Cancer Society 2020, accessed 6 July 2022, https://www.cancer.org/treatment/treatments-and-side-effects/physical-side-effects/low-blood-counts/anemia.html

American Kidney Fund, Inc. 2021, accessed 20 July 2022, https://www.kidneyfund.org/living-kidney-disease/health-problems-caused-kidney-disease/anemia-symptoms-causes-and-treatments

American Society of Hematology n.d, accessed 8 July 2022, https://www.hematology.org/education/patients/anemia

Better Health n.d, accessed 19July 2022, https://www.betterhealth.vic.gov.au/health/conditionsandtreatments/anaemia

Cleveland Clinic 2020, accessed 8 July 2022, https://my.clevelandclinic.org/health/diseases/3929-anemia

Dennis Thompson Jr 2014, Everyday Health, accessed 13 July 2022, https://www.everydayhealth.com/anemia/anemia-basics.aspx

Evan M. Braunstein , MD, PhD 2022, MSD Manual, accessed 23 July 2022, https://www.msdmanuals.com/home/blood-disorders/anemia/sickle-cell-disease

Familydoctor.org 2021, accessed 6 July 2022, https://familydoctor.org/condition/anemia/

Healthwise Staff 2021, MyHealth.Alberta.ca, accessed 11 July 2022, https://myhealth.alberta.ca/Health/aftercareinformation/pages/conditions.aspx?hwid=uf8147

References

Intermountain Healthcare n.d, accessed 20 July 2022, https://intermountainhealthcare.org/services/blood-disorders/conditions/anemia/

Jerry R. Balentine, DO, FACEP and Siamak N. Nabili, MD, MPH 2022, MedicineNet accessed 10 July 2022, https://www.medicinenet.com/anemia/article.htm

John Hopkins Medicine n.d, accessed 21 July 2022, https://www.hopkinsmedicine.org/health/conditions-and-diseases/irondeficiency-anemia

March of Dimes 2013, accessed 24 July 2022, https://www.marchofdimes.org/complications/anemia.aspx

Mayo Clinic n.d, accessed 27 July 2022, https://www.mayoclinic.org/diseases-conditions/anemia/symptoms-causes/syc-20351360#:~:text=Overview,you%20feel%20tired%20and%20weak.

MedBroadcast n.d, accessed 9 July 2022, https://medbroadcast.com/condition/getcondition/anemia

National Heart, Lung and Blood Institute 2022, accessed 11 July 2022, https://www.nhlbi.nih.gov/health/anemia

NHS 2021, accessed 7 July 2022, https://www.nhs.uk/conditions/iron-deficiency-anaemia/

PennMedicine 2020, accessed 16 July 2022, https://www.pennmedicine.org/for-patients-and-visitors/patient-information/conditions-treated-a-to-z/anemia

References

Peter Lam 2020, Medical News Today, accessed 16 July 2022, https://www.medicalnewstoday.com/articles/158800

RadiologyInfo.org 2022, accessed 8 July 2022, https://www.radiologyinfo.org/en/info/anemia

Sabrina Felson, MD 2020, WebMD, accessed 7 July 2022, https://www.webmd.com/a-to-z-guides/understanding-anemia-basics

Siamak N. Nabili, MD, MPH 2022, eMedicineHealth, accessed 15 July 2022, https://www.emedicinehealth.com/anemia/article_em.htm

Stanford n.d, accessed 17 July 2022, https://www.stanfordchildrens.org/en/topic/default?id=anemia-in-pregnancy-90-P02428

UCSF Health n.d, accessed 25 July 2022, https://www.ucsfhealth.org/education/anemia-and-pregnancy

University of Rochester Medical Center Rochester n.d, accessed 28 July 2022, https://www.urmc.rochester.edu/encyclopedia/content.aspx?contenttypeid=85&contentid=P00078

Verneda Lights and Jill Seladi-Schulman, Ph.D. 2021, Healthline, accessed 8 July 2022, https://www.healthline.com/health/anemia

World Health Organization n.d, accessed 12 July 2022, https://www.who.int/health-topics/anaemia#tab=tab_1

References

www.ingramcontent.com/pod-product-compliance
Lightning Source LLC
Chambersburg PA
CBHW071621290326
41931CB00048B/1590

* 9 7 8 1 9 5 7 3 6 7 4 6 0 *

REFRACTIONS OF LIGHT

REFRACTIONS
OF
LIGHT

201 ANSWERS ON APPARITIONS, VISIONS AND THE CATHOLIC CHURCH

BY
KEVIN J. SYMONDS

EN ROUTE BOOKS & MEDIA

En Route Books & Media
5705 Rhodes Avenue, St. Louis, MO 63109
Contact us at contactus@enroutebooksandmedia.com

Cover design by T.J. Burdick
Photo credit for the front cover is Flikr Creative Commons:
Rob, "Blue Eye" @ https:// lic.kr/p/73MQbS

Print ISBN: 978-1-950108-55-8
E-book ISBN: 978-1-63337-044-9

Printed in the United States of America

NIHIL OBSTAT: Steven J. Meyer, S.T.D., Censor
University of St. Thomas, Houston

IMPRIMATUR: +Joe S. Vásquez, S.T.L., D.D.
Bishop of Austin

The *NIHIL OBSTAT* and the *IMPRIMATUR* are a declaration that a book is considered to be free of doctrinal or moral error. It is not implied that those who have granted the *NIHIL OBSTAT* and the *IMPRIMATUR* agree with the concerns, opinions, or statements expressed therein.

—Contents—

—ACKNOWLEDGEMENTS—

I would like to thank the following people for their help in the writing of this book:

Those who assisted in the research:

- Kathleen Donohue and Linda Franklin of the John Paul II Library of the Franciscan University of Steubenville.
- Mrs. Tracy Koenig and the Eugene H. Maly Library of the Athenaeum of St. Gregory.
- The staff at Kindlon Hall of Learning at Benedictine University.
- The staff at the Charles Souvay Library at Kenrick-Glennon Seminary.
- Msgr. Christopher Lathem and Sr. Sandra Makowski from the Diocese of Charleston, SC.
- Marie Thomas from Australia.
- Mrs. Cheryl Adams of the Library of Congress.
- The Cathedral Foundation.
- Dustin Booher of the Mullen Library at the Catholic University of America.

The translators: Dr. Michael Woodward, Miss Bistra Pishtiyska-McCullough, and Mr. Matthew Sherry.

Mark Waterinckx, I am grateful for your assistance and witness.

Matthew Figured and Kate Bluett who aided the editing of the manuscript.

Monsieur Joachim Bouflet for answering critical questions.

Denise Wood and *Semper Fi Catholic* for much support over the years.

Fr. Kenneth Yossa, Ph.D., whose direction has been of inestimable value.

Miss Amanda Parker, who went over the transcription of the Latin documents with me.

The monks of St. Bernard Abbey who permitted me use of their library.

Last, but certainly not least, I wish to give thanks to our Lord and our Lady, who gave the strength and grace to inspire and see this project to its end.

Thank you to everyone who has contributed in some way to the writing of this book.

—ABBREVIATIONS—

1917 CIC = 1917 *Codex Iuris Canonici* (1917 Code of Canon Law)

1983 CIC = 1983 *Codex Iuris Canonici* (1983 Code of Canon Law)

ASS = *Acta Sanctae Sedis* (The official journal of the Holy See before 1907)

AAS = *Acta Apostolicae Sedis* (The official journal of the Holy See after 1907)

CCC = Catechism of the Catholic Church (1997, Second Edition)

CDF = Congregation for the Doctrine of the Faith (Vatican Dicastery)

Coelestis = *Coelestis Hierusalem* (1634 Papal Bull of Pope Urban VIII)

Index = *Index Librorum Prohibitorum* (Index of Forbidden Books)

EP = *Ecclesiae Pastorum* (1975 Decree of the CDF)

NC = *Normae Congregationis* (1978 Letter of the CDF)

PE = *Post Editam* (November 1966 Decree of the CDF)

PLA = *Post Litteras Apostolicas* (June 1966 Notification of the CDF)

PR = Press Release (1996 Notification of the CDF)

Sanctissimus = *Sanctissimus Dominus Noster* (1625 Papal Bull of Pope Urban VIII)

SC 1992 = *Instruction on Some Aspects of the Use of the Instruments of Social Communication in Promoting the Doctrine of the Faith* (1992 Instruction of the CDF)

—DEDICATION—

To my parents, John R. Symonds (†)
& Marjorie C. Ward.
Thank you for your many sacrifices.

To my cousins, Gary & Marleen, Tom & Janet.
Thank you for passing on the Faith to me.

To Professor Susanna DeBelli (†):
Mater et Magistra

“We…do not announce a Gospel of prosperity, but Christian realism. We do not announce miracles, as some do, but the sobriety of Christian life. We are convinced that all this sobriety and realism which announce a God Who became man…give meaning to our own suffering. In this way, announcement has a broader horizon and a greater future….The announcement of prosperity, of miraculous healing, etc., may do good in the short term, but we soon see that life is difficult, that a human God, a God Who suffers with us, is more convincing, truer, and offers greater help for life.”

—Pope Benedict XVI

“John Paul made you burst into tears.
Benedict makes you think.”

—Peggy Noonan

—PREFACE—

For the past several decades, there has been a notable rise in people claiming private revelations. The growth of these reports has often led to confusion and sensationalism among the Catholic faithful, and because of insufficient catechesis, important tenets of the Catholic faith have been largely neglected or forgotten. This has led many of the faithful to turn to private revelation for answers and solace. In order to dispel some of this confusion, I have written this book to clarify the teaching of the Church on private revelation.

I began researching claims of private revelation during my undergraduate studies. Having access to a great number of books, journals and other article sources, I began to study this subject in greater depth, and have continued in it ever since. It is my desire to share some of the fruits of my studies with the reader so that he or she may understand better the way to holiness that God has set for the faithful.

Holiness is the goal of private revelation. Holiness means a greater love for God, and the more we love God, the more we will love His Church. The Church is the depository, guardian, and dispenser of the divine mysteries, and it is by her that one comes to know and love God more. It is also true that authentic private revelation contains a message that sheds light on the divine mysteries, thereby leading us closer to God. The focus, however, is never on the private revelation but on the public mystery.

There is a danger that often accompanies private revelation: allowing it to take the place of public revelation. This is often the case in contemporary claims of private revelation. Approved private revelations are those which shed light on the Deposit of Faith, rather than casting their shadow over it. The Church and her faithful must cling, above all, to the Deposit of Faith, being always "sober and vigilant" in evaluating anything that could be contrary (1 Peter 5:8). This is a clarion call for greater exercising of the interior life of virtue.

This book is divided into three parts: Questions and Answers, Appendices and Endnotes. The Q&A forms the principal part wherein most of the primary information is conveyed. The Q&A is designed to be simple, effective and methodical in communicating the Church's theology of private revelation. The Appendices were born from a desire to provide the reader with excellent source documents about or affecting private revelation. For the purposes of this book, I have included primary sources that are either directly issued by the Magisterium or are private statements made by Church authorities.

In order to communicate this history and lore, much time and effort were spent in finding, transcribing and translating the documents. My gratitude to the translators listed above is immense. In addition to providing the translations, the original languages are also included. It is my hope that doing so might be of particular help for my readers who may have a facility in foreign languages and wish to make a comparison of the original with the translated version.

The Endnotes serve a three-fold purpose: to satisfy scholarly standards of research, give commentary and provide additional information. As much as this book is written from magisterial teachings, various theologians and commentators have written on the subject. Utilizing the greater context of Catholic theology, I have also brought to the subject my own contributions. In order to avoid blurring the lines between these three, some commentary was necessary to facilitate the text.

While researching, I discovered that a percentage of the Church's teaching comes from how she has discerned individual cases. This fact conflicted with a goal of mine to leave out references to and commentary on specific claims of private revelation by name (that is, person or place) and remain neutral by speaking objectively. This goal was rooted in my desire for the focus of this book to be on the Church's teaching. As the writing process continued, I realized the impracticality of this goal.

In light of the above, I was compelled to modify slightly the original goal by distinguishing between *approved* cases and *unapproved* ones. Approved cases are discussed by name, but not unapproved ones unless it was unavoidable. This distinction allowed me to retain my desire to focus on the Church's teaching as well as employ objective/neutral language. For referencing purposes, the terms "alleged," "supposed" and "claims to" are consistently used when speaking on unapproved claims of private revelation. When I speak about approved cases, I relax such terms.

If I offer comment in an answer or an addendum to a question that references a specific case, I am to be understood as offering a clarification of the Church's teaching. The reader will also note the terms "Vatican," "Rome" and the "Holy See" are used interchangeably. They are shorthand references to the Pope and curial departments.

This book is not meant by any means to be a comprehensive treatment of the subject. Some Church legislation and processes have changed over time. The doctrine has not changed, only how the Church treats the subject. The larger history is referenced and respected through tracing the line of consistent teaching, but the scope of the book largely limits itself to current Church legislation from Vatican II onward.

It is my sincere hope that this book will lead the reader to greater holiness. May this book be a light on the path to the Lord Jesus Christ.

In pace, benedicamus Domino!
Kevin J. Symonds, M.A.

QUESTIONS AND ANSWERS

–INTRODUCTION–

Beginning with our first parents, God revealed Himself to mankind. After the Fall of Adam and Eve, He promised them redemption. Until that time, God continued to reveal Himself through the patriarchs and prophets. When that time came, God sent forth His Son, born of a woman, born under the law, to redeem those who were under the law, so that we might receive adoption as sons (Galatians 4:4). In Christ, God has said everything and there will be no other word than this one (CCC 65).

No new public revelation is to be expected before the glorious manifestation of our Lord Jesus Christ (CCC 66). It remains for Christian faith gradually to grasp its full significance over the course of the centuries (CCC 66). God has revealed Himself once and for all in Christ and He continues to speak to His people so as to help them live the Gospel in a particular moment in history. Such moments in time are better known as "private revelations." It is this topic that the present book seeks to explain and discuss.

The Church takes Jesus' command to preach the Gospel to all nations very seriously (Matthew 28:16-20). Throughout the centuries, she has defended the teachings of Christ and safeguarded them against error and falsehood. A particular error she has fought against is the claim to "another Gospel" (Galatians 1:6-9). One of the most serious dangers posed by private revelation is when it is presented as another Gospel. The Church has been careful to protect the faithful against the possibility of being led astray by such claims.

To safeguard the revelation of God to man, the Church has clearly defined her teaching over the centuries. Her theology of private revelation is no different. The Church has had to explain the nature and purpose of private revelation as well as establish clear guidelines and processes. These help Christians to maintain faith and good morals in preparation for heaven. A few examples are of interest for the purposes of this book.

Older Catholics might remember the Index of Forbidden Books and the system of censorship it engendered. For younger Catholics, the Index was a list of books that Catholics were forbidden to read without special permission. The present book offers an intimate presentation of the Index, its *raison d'etre*, and its history in relation to private revelation. The purpose of this presentation is to give rise to discussion on the moral duties and obligations of Catholics with matters concerning faith and morals.

In addition, the reforms of Pope Paul VI to the Church's system of censorship are presented and treatment is provided for the difficult questions that arise as a result of his reforms. Questions such as the moral obligation to seek censorship for matter touching upon faith and morals are the type found in this book. Furthermore, significant attention is paid to the Congregation for the Doctrine of the Faith's 1978 Letter "*Normae S. Congregationis*" on discerning apparitions and revelations.

This book has two objectives: to help Catholics learn more about their faith and to understand certain moral duties and obligations to help them get to heaven. The primary mode for this is in the questions and answers (Q&A). Numbering 201 in total, the Q&A covers all of the above areas of discussion as well as various questions pertinent to the subject of this book. The Q&A is designed for any Catholic to read regardless of their theological training. Concepts are explained and key words given and defined. Many questions are written consecutively, so the reader may have to read preceding questions to follow the train of thought.

1. What is private revelation?

"Private revelation is the supernatural manifestation of a hidden truth by means of a vision, a word, or only a prophetic instinct...."[1] The term "refers to all the visions and revelations that have taken place since the completion of the New Testament."[2]

2. What is the purpose of private revelation?

The purpose of private revelation is to provide emphasis on a particular aspect of the Gospel at a specific moment in time so as to lead the faithful to a deepening of faith, hope and charity/love.[3]

3. How does the Church respond to claims of private revelations?

The Church exercises great caution with respect to claims of private revelations as she follows the Apostolic mandate to "test the spirits."[4] It is also commonly said that the Church "moves slowly in these matters."

4. Does the Church have processes to discern alleged private revelations?

Yes, in 1978 the Congregation for the Doctrine of the Faith (hereafter, CDF) issued privately a document on how to proceed to discern alleged private revelations.[5] This document is entitled *Normae S. Congregationis* (hereafter, NC).[6]

5. What are those procedures?

The procedures given in NC are divided into five parts and are as follows:

1. A preliminary note.
2. A list of positive and negative criteria to use in judging the character of alleged revelations.
3. How the competent Ecclesiastical Authority is to proceed.
4. On the Authorities entitled to intervene.
5. On the intervention of the CDF.

6. What does the preliminary note say?

The preliminary note establishes the origin and character of the norms contained within NC. It discusses why the document was written. It also provides an overview of the way alleged private revelations are to be discerned.

7. How are alleged private revelations to be discerned?

NC has two, three-tiered structures that claims to private revelations can go through.

8. What is the first structure?

The first structure concerns the competent Ecclesiastical Authority and is delineated as follows:

1. The local Ordinary.
2. The Conference of Bishops (or Synod in the Eastern Churches).
3. The CDF and the Pope.[7]

9. What is the second structure?

The second structure concerns the process of discernment and approbation of an alleged private revelation. It is delineated as follows:

1. Initial judgment on the facts using positive and negative criteria.
2. Permission may be given for certain public demonstrations of cult and devotion while still investigating the facts in question (otherwise known as the "response of the faithful").
3. Full judgment on the supernatural character of the supposed events.[8]

10. What are the negative criteria?

The negative criteria are as follows:

1. Manifest error concerning the fact.
2. Doctrinal errors attributed to God, the Virgin Mary or saints in their manifestations.
   a. Vigilance is necessary against the possibility of human additions or errors being made in the alleged revelations.
3. Evidence of a gain of profit strictly connected to the fact.
4. The alleged visionary or followers commit gravely immoral acts at the time of the alleged revelation or on their occasion.
5. The alleged visionary demonstrates psychic disorders or psychopathic tendencies that clearly influenced the allegedly supernatural fact.[9]

11. What are the positive criteria?

The positive criteria are as follows:

1. There exists moral certitude or at least great probability the alleged revelations are real.
2. The one claiming revelations demonstrates:
   a. psychological equilibrium,
   b. honesty and rectitude of moral life,
   c. sincerity and habitual docility towards Ecclesiastical Authority, and
   d. capacity for returning to the normal regimen of a life of faith
3. There is true theological and spiritual doctrine and immunity from error.
4. There is healthy devotion and abundant and constant spiritual fruit.[10]

12. In the negative criteria, what is meant by a "manifest error about the fact"?

A "manifest error about the event" means a clear error cannot be present in claims to private revelation, such as in relaying the sequence of events/giving false testimony.[11]

13. Why must vigilance be taken against human additions in alleged private revelations?

A person may offer his or her own impressions or commentary to what he/she allegedly saw or heard so as to elucidate the meaning. This impression or commentary can err.[12]

14. What is the "natural order" and why is it a concern for alleged private revelations?

The natural order is the created world. If any human addition to alleged private revelations contradicts that order, doubt is cast upon the alleged revelations.

15. Why must alleged private revelations be immune from theological and spiritual error in doctrine?

Alleged private revelations must be free from error in the above areas because God cannot contradict Himself. What He has established for our salvation does not change.

16. Why are the alleged visionary's followers included as affecting the discernment of an alleged private revelation?

The reason is because there is a connection between the alleged visionary, the alleged phenonmena and the way devotion that originated in the claims is practiced.[13]

17. What are some examples of psychopathic tendencies that would clearly exercise an influence upon the claims?

Some examples of such tendencies would be schizophrenia and severe depression.

18. Under the positive criteria, what is meant by a "capacity for returning to the normal regimen of a life of faith"?

The above capacity means persons claiming to be receiving private revelations do not make their alleged revelations the goal or end of their Christian lives. Rather, they can be consistently found doing things "common" to Catholic life, practice, duty, and piety.

19. What are some indications that a person claiming to be receiving private revelations returns to the normal regimen of a life of faith?

Some indications would be as follows. The person:

1. attends Mass regularly in accordance with his or her state in life,
2. obeys the precepts of the Church,
3. converses with those around him or her, and
4. maintains a healthy prayer life.

20. Are the negative and positive criteria meant to be the only criteria the Church uses in her discernment of alleged private revelations?

No, the criteria mentioned in NC, "are not peremptory but rather indicative, and they should be applied cumulatively or with some mutual convergence."[14] For instance, there is nothing in NC about miracles as a criterion, yet they have a role in the discernment of a case.[15]

21. Is there a fundamental principle by which the Church discerns alleged private revelations?

There is a fundamental principle that the Church uses to discern alleged private revelations:

> The criterion for the truth and value of [alleged] private revelation is...its orientation to Christ himself. When

it leads us away from him, when it becomes independent of him or even presents itself as another and better plan of salvation, more important than the Gospel, then it certainly does not come from the Holy Spirit, who guides us more deeply into the Gospel and not away from it. This does not mean that a private revelation will not offer new emphases or give rise to new devotional forms, or deepen and spread older forms. But in all of this there must be a nurturing of faith, hope and love, which are the unchanging path to salvation for everyone.[16]

22. Who determines if alleged private revelations are from God or not?

The competent Ecclesiastical Authority determines the character of such claims.

23. Who is the "competent Ecclesiastical Authority"?

There are three such Authorities: the local Ordinary, the conference of bishops and the Holy See.[17] Of these, the local Ordinary is the foremost judge of any such claims.[18]

24. What is a "local Ordinary"?

The local Ordinary is:

1. the Holy Father.
2. a diocesan bishop.
3. one placed over some particular church or equivalent community, or
4. those who possess general Ordinary executive power.[19]

25. When can a local Ordinary intervene in alleged private revelations?

There are four ways a local Ordinary can intervene.

26. In what four ways can a local Ordinary intervene?

The four ways are as follows: [20]

1. When devotion on the part of the faithful begins quasi-spontaneously because of alleged private revelations.
2. The faithful request the competent Ecclesiastical Authority to intervene.
3. When grave circumstances warrant immediate intervention of the Ecclesiastical Authority.
4. The Ecclesiastical Authority may also refrain from making any judgment and taking any direct action.

27. What would constitute "grave circumstances" for a local Ordinary to intervene immediately?

NC provides three non-exhaustive circumstances for this intervention. They are:

1. when it is a question of correcting or warning against abuses in the exercise of worship or devotion,
2. to condemn erroneous doctrines, or
3. to avoid the dangers of a false or disorderly mysticism.[21]

28. When would a local Ordinary refrain from any judgment or direct action?

A local Ordinary could refrain from judgment or direct action when the case is "doubtful" and makes "little difference to the good of the Church."[22]

29. Does the above mean the local Ordinary should not keep informed of developments?

The local Ordinary should "not cease from being vigilant, by intervening if necessary, with promptness and prudence."[23]

30. What does the term "supernatural" mean?

The term "supernatural" is the divine life of God over and

above the natural order in which we live. "The Supernatural Order is the ensemble of effects exceeding the powers of the created universe and gratuitously produced by God for the purpose of raising the rational creature above its native sphere to a God-like life and destiny."[24]

31. What then does "supernatural" mean in the theology of private revelation?

In the theology of private revelation, the term "supernatural" means three things:

1. The alleged private revelations are truly from God.
2. They are declared to be such by the authority of the Church.
3. The faithful can trust in the authenticity of the claims if they so choose.

32. Why is it that, "...the faithful can trust...*if they so choose*"?

The faithful are not bound to believe in alleged private revelations.[25]

33. Why are the faithful not bound to believe in alleged private revelations, especially if approved?

The teaching of the Church distinguishes between "public revelation" (also known as "divine revelation") and "private revelation(s)."[26] Catholics are required to believe in the former but not the latter.

34. What is the distinction between "public" and "private" revelation?

According to the CDF, the distinction between the two is as follows:

> The term "public revelation" refers to the revealing action of God directed to humanity as a whole and which

> finds its literary expression in the two parts of the Bible: the Old and New Testaments. It is called "Revelation" because in it God gradually made himself known to men, to the point of becoming man himself, in order to draw to himself the whole world and unite it with himself through his Incarnate Son, Jesus Christ.[27]

Public revelation "demands faith" and private revelation "is a help to that faith."[28] It is not that faith in itself.

35. Does believing in alleged private revelations mean a person has put faith in them?

Yes, however there is a distinction the Church makes about the *kind* of "faith" placed in claims to private revelations.

36. What is the distinction about the kind of faith placed in alleged private revelations?

The distinction is between "divine" or "Catholic" faith and "human" faith. According to Prospero Cardinal Lambertini (later Pope Benedict XIV):

> An assent of Catholic faith is not due to revelations approved in this way; it is not even possible. These revelations seek rather an assent of human faith in keeping with the requirements of prudence, which puts them before us as probable and credible to piety.[29]

This means there is a difference between the theological virtue of faith (see question 91) and human faith. An individual can believe in alleged private revelations on human faith but he or she does not give the assent of divine or Catholic faith, which is given only to divine revelation.

37. If alleged private revelations contain a message of worldwide importance, must the faithful believe in the alleged message?

The Church distinguishes between "obligation" and "disregard" with respect to an alleged private revelation:

> [s]uch a message [i.e. alleged private revelations] can be a genuine help in understanding the Gospel and living it better at a particular moment in time; therefore it should not be disregarded. It is a help which is offered, but which one is not obliged to use.[30]

38. What is the distinction between "obliged" and "disregarded"?

Legitimate private revelations should not be taken lightly. God has offered them for a reason and the faithful should seriously consider the message being given. However, private revelations (whether legitimate or fraudulent) do not enjoy an obligatory character—the faithful are not *obliged* to believe in them.

39. What is the role of the Vatican in the discernment of alleged private revelations?

The Holy Father/the CDF have the right to intervene in claims of private revelations. This may happen in one of three ways:

1. The local Ordinary requests the Vatican's intervention.
2. A qualified group of the faithful petitions the Holy See.
3. A case takes on a "grave" nature, requiring the Vatican to intervene in virtue of its universal jurisdiction.[31]

40. Does Rome judge the character of the alleged private revelations?

Rome will intervene and judge a claim if it is necessary and at least one of the conditions given in question 39 is met.[32]

41. Why will Rome intervene only under the above conditions?

Rome will intervene only under the above conditions because it is not the initial judge of the character of any claim.[33]

42. Since the promulgation of NC, has the Vatican exercised its universal jurisdiction in claims to private revelations that are not grave?

The Vatican has not exercised its universal jurisdiction to intervene in non-grave cases of alleged private revelations.

43. What qualifies as a "grave" case for the Vatican to intervene on its own authority?

A "grave" case means when the (supposed) event "affects a large part of the Church."[34]

44. Since the promulgation of NC, has there been at least one grave case wherein the Vatican intervened of its own authority?

Yes, the Vatican has intervened of its own authority in at least one grave case since the promulgation of NC.[35]

45. Does the discernment of claims to private revelations have to go to the conference of bishops or the Vatican?

The local Ordinary is under no obligation to go to the conference of bishops or the Vatican, though the Ordinary would be wise to seek their help if the case required it.[36]

46. When would the conference of bishops become involved?

NC clearly states only two points at which the conference of bishops could become involved. They are as follows:[37]

1. The local Ordinary resorts to the conference after having fulfilled his obligations.
2. The event assumes national or regional importance.

47. If the case comes to the competence of the conference of bishops or the Pope, does the local Ordinary remain involved with the discernment?

In order to answer this question, a distinction must be made between the authority of the local conference and the authority of the Pope.

48. What is the distinction between the authority of the conference and the authority of the Pope?

Of itself, the local conference does not have the authority to render an official judgment on the character of an alleged private revelation, whereas the Holy Father does.

49. Why does the Holy Father render judgment on the character of a claim but not the local conference of bishops?

The reason for the distinction is because the authority of the Catholic Church resides in the College of Bishops united to the Holy Father as its head.

50. Does this mean that local conferences of bishops are not part of the structure of the Church?

The conferences are not part of this structure.[38]

51. What then is the purpose of the local conference's intervention if it cannot issue a binding judgment?

The purpose of the local conference's intervention is to assist the local Ordinary in making a "safer judgment of the matter."[39]

52. What then is the role of a local Ordinary if the Pope was examining a case so as to make a judgment?

A lower Authority should not intervene in the matter without grave cause.[40] It remains, however, at the discretion of the higher Authority to involve the local Ordinary in the matter.

53. Can a local Ordinary approve part of the message of alleged private revelations and not other parts?

No. Ordinaries do not approve parts of alleged private revelations.

54. Why does a local Ordinary not approve part of an alleged message?

The whole message must be taken into consideration so as to weigh properly the content of faith and morals. [41]

55. Has a local Ordinary approved earlier private revelations but not others alleged to have happened later to the same person?

Yes, local Ordinaries have approved private revelations that have occurred earlier and not approved or judged alleged later ones. For instance, Sr. Lúcia, the last visionary of Fátima, allegedly received later private revelations but only those from May-October, 1917 were declared to be supernatural by the local Ordinary.

56. Why would a local Ordinary not judge later alleged private revelations?

It is a simple matter of timing and need. Sometimes there is no need for a judgment as the case may not affect the good of the Church.

57. Would the later claims require another examination or would they be seen in tandem with the approved revelations?

Later claims would require another examination, which may or may not end in a positive judgment.

58. Are not the later alleged revelations integral to the original examination?

Not necessarily. The original approved claims are supernatural (according to the earlier definition). The alleged later ones may or may not also be supernatural.

59. Why would the alleged later ones not be supernatural?

It could be the visionary, regrettably, became corrupt later in life and decided to seek, for example, monetary gain or popularity by alleging further revelations.

60. If a claimant was to become corrupt later in life, would that call into question the earlier approved revelations?

While such actions would be utterly tragic, the original revelations would not be called into question.[42] For instance, Melanie Mathieu, one of the visionaries of La Salette in France, later wrote an apocryphal "secret" that was condemned by the Vatican in 1915.[43] The original examination, however, was not affected by this later condemnation and La Salette is held to be supernatural in origin.

61. Must a local Ordinary only render judgment on the supernatural character of a claim when the alleged phenomenon ceases?

A distinction must be made between a *positive* judgment and a *negative* judgment.

62. What is the distinction between a positive and negative judgment?

A local Ordinary does not have to wait until the alleged phenomenon ceases before he can give a *negative* judgment. He may not make a *positive* judgment while the alleged events are still happening.

63. What is the reason for the distinction?

Matter contrary to faith and morals might manifest while the alleged revelations are "ongoing." If no such contrary matter has been found and the alleged revelations are ongoing, then it would not be prudent to judge positively that which could later obtain contrary matter.

64. Could the local Ordinary wait until a claim ceases before rendering a negative judgment?

Yes, the local Ordinary could wait until a claim ceases before rendering a negative judgment, provided there is no existing matter contrary to faith and morals.

65. What would be the purpose to wait for a claim to cease?

Waiting is a "prudential" action allowing all the facts to be considered. It is not an absolute rule.

66. Have negative judgments on the character of a claim been rendered while the alleged phenomenon was still occurring?

Yes, negative judgments have been rendered while the alleged phenomenon was still occurring. These judgments, many with Rome's consultation, are still in effect.

67. How does the local Ordinary investigate a claim?

Typically, a commission of competent persons is established to investigate a claim. If one is established, its findings are reported to the local Ordinary for his judgment.[44]

68. In what manner is a judgment made on the supernatural character of a claim to private revelations?

After investigating the facts of a case, the local Ordinary renders his judgment publicly by way of one of three Latin expressions: [45]

1. *Constat de supernaturalitate,*
2. *Non constat de supernaturalitate, or*
3. *Constat de non supernaturalitate.*

69. What is "*constat de supernaturalitate*"?

This means "consists of the supernatural." It is a positive judgment stating the claims are supernatural in origin.

70. What is "*non constat de supernaturalitate*"?

This literally means "consists not of the supernatural." This judgment is interpreted to mean a straightforward positive or negative judgment cannot be made at the time.

71. What is "*constat de non supernaturalitate*"?

This literally means "consists of no supernatural." This judgment states a claim does not have a supernatural origin.

72. If "*non constat de supernaturalitate*" is given, does that mean the case is open for further examination?

Yes, the case is open for a later, more definitive judgment after further examination.[46]

73. If a local Ordinary rendered a negative verdict on a claim but did not establish a commission, is the judgment binding?

If the local Ordinary has judged positively or negatively on alleged private revelations, his judgment is binding regardless of whether a commission was established.

74. Since the promulgation of NC, has the Vatican overruled the judgment of the local Ordinary on the supernatural character of an alleged private revelation?

The Vatican has not overruled the judgment of a local Ordinary since the promulgation of NC.[47]

75. What potential dangers can alleged private revelations create?

The Church is concerned the faithful may become driven by a "sectarian spirit" that divides the Mystical Body of Christ.[48]

76. What is a "sectarian spirit"?

"Sectarian spirit" is not defined, but context dictates it is a spirit or attitude that divides the faithful from obedience and communion with their Pastors.[49]

77. Is it permissible for the faithful to go against Ecclesiastical Authority in order to ensure an alleged message is made known?

It is not permissible for the faithful to go against Ecclesiastical Authority in order to ensure an alleged message is made known.

78. Why is it not permissible?

The faithful are called to obey their Pastors who are the ones who determine whether an alleged private revelation is supernatural or not. Hence if the competent Ecclesiastical Authority has issued a guideline or statement on a claim, the faithful must obey.[50]

79. May Catholics disregard a directive on alleged private revelations issued by a local Ordinary who does not or is said not to believe in *any* private revelation?

The faithful may not disregard a directive by the local Ordinary even though he may not be inclined to believe in any private revelation.

80. What if there is a just reason to re-investigate a case?

If there is a just reason to re-investigate the facts, the faithful have a right to make their legitimate needs known to the Pastors of the Church, even to the Holy See directly. NC gives a proper protocol in such instances.

81. What is the above-mentioned proper protocol?

A "qualified group of the faithful" can petition Rome to intervene.[51]

82. Who is considered "qualified" to make such a petition?

The term can refer to stable associations recognized by Ecclesiastical Authority as well as private associations of the Christian faithful.[52]

83. Does asking Rome to intervene mean the faithful are disregarding the local Ordinary and breaking with charity?

Unless the request is made in a sectarian spirit, no, it does not mean a qualified group of the faithful is disregarding the local Ordinary, much less showing disrespect toward him or being uncharitable.[53]

84. What if Rome affirms the decision of the local Ordinary?

If Rome were to affirm the local Ordinary in his decision, the faithful are bound and obliged to cease and desist believing in and promoting the alleged private revelations.

85. What if the faithful still adhere to the alleged revelations even after Rome affirms the local Ordinary's decision?

They should be earnestly prayed for so that they return to the bonds of charity and unity with the Church.[54]

86. How does a local Ordinary's statement, guideline or judgment on alleged private revelations canonically affect Catholics and other Ordinaries throughout the world when the first Ordinary only has juridical authority over the flock entrusted to him?

Generally (but not always), a rule or precept issued by an Ordinary only has binding authority over those who are physically present within his geographical jurisdiction.[55] For their part, the interior life of virtue and the general precept of unity in the Catholic faith mandate the faithful be united in charity with the Universal Church.[56]

87. What does it mean to be united in charity with the Universal Church as it pertains to alleged private revelations?

To be united in charity with the Universal Church in this instance means if a local Ordinary issues a statement on alleged private revelations in his jurisdiction, no priest, abbot, bishop or layman—all being bound to prudence and charity—would be wise to declare through word or deed that the Ordinary is wrong and thereby disrupt communion with him.[57]

88. What happens if that communion is disrupted?

If that communion is disrupted, unity becomes weakened and serves the "sectarian spirit" spoken of earlier.[58]

89. What "word or deed" constitutes declaring the local Ordinary to be wrong?

A direct opposing statement could constitute this as well as traveling to the place where said revelations are claimed to be occurring.

90. What virtue or virtues must be practiced by the Catholic faithful in response to claims of alleged private revelations?

All the virtues must be practiced as all of them are interconnected. There are, however, some particular virtues in connection with alleged private revelations.

91. What particular virtues are in connection with alleged private revelations?

These virtues are: faith, charity, humility, obedience, prudence, justice and temperance.

92. Why are the above virtues stressed?

The above virtues are stressed because of their proximity to the subject:

Faith is the theological virtue by which we believe in God and believe all that He has said and revealed to us, and that Holy Church proposes for our belief, because He is truth itself. By faith man freely commits his entire self to God. He completely submits his intellect and his will to God. With his whole being man gives his assent to God the revealer. Sacred Scripture calls this human response to God, the author of revelation, "the obedience of faith."[60] Knowing the contents of divine revelation is critical in any discernment of supposed private revelations that could contradict that revelation.[61]

Charity is the greatest of the theological virtues.[62] By it, the faithful love God above all things for his own sake, and their neighbor as themselves for the love of God.[63] The practice of all the virtues is animated and inspired by charity.[64] Charity leads us to render to God what we as creatures owe Him in all justice.[65] Charity protects the faithful from developing a "sectarian spirit" thinking that they know better than the Church.

Humility is the virtue by which a Christian acknowledges that God is the author of all good. Humility avoids inordinate ambition or pride, and provides the foundation for turning to God in prayer.[66] Prayer depends especially on the grace of God; hence we prepare for it far less by processes, which might remain mechanical, than by humility, for "God…giveth grace to the humble, and He makes us humble in order to load us with his gifts."[67] "Humility is considered in all Christian tradition as the foundation of the spiritual life, since it removes pride, which is…the beginning of every sin because it separates us from God…."[68] Humility guards the faithful against becoming proud of any alleged spiritual gifts they may have received, in particular if a soul is said to be receiving private revelations.

Obedience is the response to legitimate authority. All authority comes from God and He has placed people in positions of authority. Obeying them is obeying God and this is pleasing to Him. It is the virtue by which "the faithful submit freely to the word that has been heard, because its truth is guaranteed by God, who is Truth itself."[69] "Having become a member of the Church, the person baptized belongs no longer to himself, but to him who died and rose for us. From now on, he is called to be subject to others, to serve them in the communion of the Church, and to 'obey and submit' to the Church's leaders, holding them in respect and affection."[70]

Prudence guards the faithful against the extreme of sensationalism—getting caught up in wild claims and any thrills of spiritual titillation too often involved in supposed private revelations. The Catechism teaches about prudence:

> Prudence is the virtue that disposes practical reason to discern our true good in every circumstance and to choose the right means of achieving it....[I]t guides the other virtues by setting rule and measure. It is prudence that immediately guides the judgment of conscience. The prudent man determines and directs his conduct in accordance with this judgment. With the help of this virtue we apply moral principles to particular cases without error and overcome doubts about the good to achieve and the evil to avoid.[71]

"Faith is nourished and protected by prudence and vigilance."[72]

Justice is "the moral virtue that consists in the constant and firm will to give their due to God and neighbor."[73] It is by this virtue that the Catholic faithful render to God what is His. The faithful should not worship false gods and have improper devotions that lead away from the worship of the one true God. There is, in supposed private revelations, a distinct possibility of leading the faithful astray and thus they must be mindful of their duty of justice to God.

Temperance is "the moral virtue that moderates the attraction of pleasures and provides balance in the use of created goods."[74] Temperance protects the Catholic faithful from obsession with alleged private revelations and all sorts of devotions that could distract from faith and justice, thus preserving charity.

93. Is there a prominent virtue in connection with alleged private revelations?

Though all of the virtues are important in discernment, there are *two* fundamental virtues in discerning alleged private revelations: humility and obedience.[75]

94. Why are obedience and humility the fundamental virtues?

The purpose of legitimate private revelations is to lead the faithful to greater holiness, including the person said to be receiving the alleged revelations. Pride is the deadliest sin and humility is necessary to combat it. Obedience safeguards against self-will. If a person is possessed of his or her own self-will and not obedient to the Church and her representatives, such actions are sure signs of pride and disobedience.[76] These actions are critical in the discernment of alleged private revelations.[77]

95. How should a person claiming to be receiving private revelations report their alleged experience(s)?

The appropriate and virtuous act of any individual possibly favored with private revelations would be to report humbly the alleged phenomena to the competent Ecclesiastical Authority without making a show. The individual is then bound to obey the directive(s) of said Authority.[78]

96. Is it possible for a local Ordinary to err in his negative or positive judgment of the supernatural character of a claim to private revelation?

Yes, it is possible for a local Ordinary or even Rome to err in either a positive or negative judgment on the supernatural character of a claim to private revelation within the powers of the ordinary magisterium.

97. If the Church is infallible in matters of faith and morals, how is it possible for her to make an error regarding the supernatural character of a claim to private revelations?

The Church does not enjoy providential protection in the area of private revelations.[79] They are not a matter of the Deposit of Faith (i.e. divine revelation), in which the Church does have infallibility.

98. If a local Ordinary or Rome could be wrong on the matter, what authority do they have to judge an alleged private revelation?

The Pastors of the Church have a divine mandate to protect the faithful from errors in faith and morals. Their authority to judge the supernatural character of a claim to private revelations rests upon that mandate and that of the faithful to obey them when they make an authoritative ruling. Thus, if a local Ordinary saw negative elements in a devotion spurred by an alleged private revelation, for example, he could call the faithful back to the teachings of the Gospel and that is a legitimate exercise of his authority.[80]

99. Is it common for a local Ordinary or Rome to reverse negative judgments?

It is *very* rare for negative judgments to be overturned.[81]

100. Are there some general reasons for negative decisions becoming reversed?

There are a few ways negative decisions could be reversed, all of which depend upon why the negative decision was given in the first place.

101. What are some of those reasons?

There are two in particular that stand out:

1. A local Ordinary might have received false information about a claim to private revelations and made a negative judgment based upon the information he possessed at that time. If false information is discovered and brought to the attention of the Ordinary, a new examination can occur.
2. It is possible that promoters of alleged private revelations have promoted devotion wrongly, before the local Ordinary approved any alleged messages. Any devotion observed in such a situation could be suppressed.

102. Why could the devotion be suppressed?

Suppressing the devotion leaves open the possibility of reviving it after some time to determine the false information through examination. Think of it as when a computer slows down after being on too long. It is shut down to reboot and when started again, runs smoothly (hopefully).

103. Is there a distinction between "devotion" and "messages"?

Yes, there is a distinction between "devotion" and "messages" as regards supposed private revelations.[82]

104. What is the distinction between the two?

"*Devotion*" means there is a legitimate form of worship (including veneration) or title of a heavenly figure as separate from claims to private revelations.

"*Messages*" means there are alleged messages from a supposed heavenly figure. These "messages" must be discerned to see if they contain matter contrary to faith and morals. This discernment can be a long process.

105. Why is there a distinction?

The general theological reasoning stands upon proposing authentic devotion for the faithful. Bishops, for instance, may want to promote authentic devotion to Jesus, Mary or other heavenly figures through legitimate means in keeping with divine revelation.[83] Some alleged apparitions of persons, for instance, have requested they be known by some title and devotion to them under that title be promoted. A bishop may want to promote devotion to a particular heavenly figure under that title, but not endorse the alleged private revelations as further discernment is required.[84]

106. Could it be that the above distinctions may be lost on the faithful due to an association made in their minds and hearts between the alleged messages and the devotion?

If a local Ordinary makes this distinction, he must ensure the faithful know the difference between the devotion and the alleged messages.[85] The purpose is to separate a potential harm from good, "for devotion to match its doctrinal content."[86]

107. How are the faithful to proceed when the local Ordinary makes such a distinction?

The faithful, as always, must pay close attention to and obey the local Ordinary in what he says and teaches.[87] They should never presume anything outside of what he has said on the matter.

108. If there is a doubt about a directive on alleged private revelations, what can be done to obtain a clarification?

If such a doubt exists, the faithful can utilize their right to make their legitimate needs known to the Pastors of the Church through the proper channels.

109. What are the proper channels?

Ideally, and for instance on the diocesan level, "proper channels" means communicating the doubt to one's parish priest who would then proceed to bring the doubt to the bishop (if the Pastor himself was not able to clarify the matter).

110. What should the faithful do until a clarification is given?

Until a clarification is given, prudence dictates the faithful exercise caution with respect to actions taken towards alleged private revelations.

111. What is the "response of the faithful" mentioned in question seven?

The "response of the faithful" means there is an ongoing examination into a claim of private revelations and that after the first stage of discernment nothing contrary to faith and morals has been found. The local Ordinary then proposes the devotion or alleged messages (see Question 103) to the faithful so as to discern the matter further.[88]

112. Is the "response of the faithful" a necessary part of testing the spirits?

The response of the faithful can be a part of testing the spirits but is not a *necessary* part. This is because the content of the alleged revelation(s) could contain matter contrary to faith and morals. Such matter can be noticed in the first stage of examination by the local Ordinary or with the help of a commission (if he chooses to have one).

113. Do not most contemporary claims to alleged private revelations quickly become a matter of public knowledge given that news of such phenomena spreads quickly today?

Yes, oftentimes such claims quickly become a matter of public knowledge and the Church recognizes this fact.[89]

114. If the Church recognizes the above, what does the Church teach as to how should the faithful proceed in such instances?

The Church expects the faithful to obey the natural law and not expose themselves to matter contrary to faith and morals. This also applies to matter that *could be* contrary. The Church also expects the faithful to follow ecclesiastical law and help Ordinaries in their mission of safeguarding faith and morals.[90]

115. What are the natural and ecclesiastical laws?

The natural law is "the eternal law of God as imprinted in rational creatures, inclining them towards the end and the actions suitable to their nature."[91]

Ecclesiastical law "is that which has been established by the Church for the spiritual welfare of the faithful."[92]

116. The faithful being bound to these laws, what should they do when they learn of alleged private revelations before an examination?

The faithful must practice virtue, especially prudence, as well as obey the laws of the Church.[93] In everything, they must demonstrate unity and charity with the local Ordinary and wait for his judgment.[94]

117. Are the faithful losing opportunities for grace by waiting upon the local Ordinary?

No, it is not true to say the faithful are losing opportunities for grace.

118. Why is it not true to say that by waiting the faithful are losing grace?

The faithful are not losing grace because, "[V]isions are not like sacraments that produce their effect by their own power in those who do not place an obstacle [to sacramental grace]…. There is no grace to be had by disobeying. To wait will not entail any loss at all, rather, God's favor will be upon those who obey."[95]

119. Is it possible for a local Ordinary to miss errors in faith and morals in the first stage of examination and then propose devotion or alleged messages to the faithful?

Yes, such a mistake is possible.

120. How could a local Ordinary make such a mistake?

There are a number of reasons such a mistake could be made. A few examples are:

1. Human frailty.
2. Excessive familiarity with the claimant.
3. Poor judgment.
4. Unobjective investigators.
5. An unthorough examination.

121. If errors in faith and morals were noticed in the second stage of examination, how should the error be exposed?

The appropriate action would be for the error to be brought to the attention of the local Ordinary or to Rome (if the case requires it).

122. Would not correcting the mistake in this way take a long time, thus possibly imperiling the faith and morals of the faithful exposed to the error?

It is possible for the process of manifesting the mistake to take some time. Thus it is encumbent upon those involved to see to a swift but judicious process.

123. What happens after the error is pointed out to the local Ordinary?

If an error in faith and morals is indeed discovered after due process, then the Ordinary has the duty to correct the error immediately and make this known to the faithful.

124. What would happen to any alleged messages or devotion after the error is corrected?

There should be no further dissemination of any messages or devotion.

125. In order to protect faith and morals, can anyone who notices such an error in these make it known directly to the faithful?

There are many facts and considerations that would have to be present in individual cases before an appropriate course of action could be taken.

126. What is one fact or consideration?

The Church's moral theology teaches everyone has the right to a good name and reputation.[96] To expose publicly the mistake of the local Ordinary could unnecessarily embarrass and humiliate him as well as damage his good name, to say nothing of creating further scandal among the faithful.

127. Pope Urban VIII is often quoted as saying about alleged private revelations, "It is better to believe than not to believe." Did he say actually say this?

To date, there is no known available evidence Pope Urban VIII made this statement.[97]

128. Where did the alleged quote come from?

It is not known how the supposed quote of Pope Urban originated, as the quote has undergone a rapid multiplication over a relatively short period of time.

129. Why then is Urban's name mentioned in connection with private revelation?

Urban VIII issued two Papal Bulls entitled, *Sanctissimus Dominus Noster* (hereafter, *Sanctissimus*) on March 13, 1625 and *Coelestis Hierusalem* (hereafter, *Coelestis*) on July 5, 1634. Both of these documents concerned—in part—papal legislation on alleged private revelations.

130. What legislation was passed in *Sanctissimus* and *Coelestis*?

Sanctissimus and *Coelestis* forbade the dissemination of materials promoting alleged private revelations without permission from the local Ordinary or the Apostolic See.

131. How did Urban's legislation affect the Church's teaching on private revelation?

This legislation became a standard part of Canon Law for over three-hundred years and also affected subsequent papal teaching on the subject. The legislation eventually became codified in the 1917 *Code of Canon Law* (hereafter 1917 CIC) under the laws of censorship.[98]

132. What is "censorship"?

Censorship is the process of scrutinizing some means of social communication that touches upon faith or morals in order to see if there is any error contrary to these.[99]

133. What is meant by "means of social communication"?

"Social communications" is the term used by the Vatican in its official documents (especially in Canon Law) to refer to a broad range of communication methods such as television, radio, the Internet, telephone, etc.

134. What would happen if matter contrary to faith and morals were found?

If matter contrary to faith and morals has been discovered, the Church has the right and duty to mandate the error(s) be corrected.[100]

135. How is the error corrected?

How the error is corrected and what the response of the Church is will largely depend upon a number of factors such as:

1. The person making the error.
2. The circumstances of the offense.
3. The specific means of social communication utilized to spread the error.[101]

136. Why do many books promoting alleged private revelations also contain a disclaimer about the Index of Forbidden Books and the abrogation of canons 1399 and 2318?

The disclaimer referenced above is often put into books on alleged private revelations owing to an interpretation of two actions made by Pope Paul VI in 1966 to reform the Church's system of censorship in accordance with the decrees of the Second Vatican Council.

137. What actions were taken by Pope Paul VI in 1966 to reform the system of censorship?

On June 14, 1966, Pope Paul VI approved a Notification from the CDF entitled *Post Litteras Apostolicas* (hereafter, PLA). This document removed the legal force of the Index of Forbidden Books. Then on November 15, 1966, Paul VI approved a Decree of the CDF entitled *Post Editam* (hereafter, PE). This decree abrogated Canons 1399 and 2318 of the 1917 CIC.

138. What is the Index of Forbidden Books?

From 1564 to 1965, the Church kept a list of books called the *Index Librorum Prohibitorum* (Index of Forbidden Books, also known as the Index). The Index was the method chosen by the Church at that time to alert the faithful to matter contrary to faith and morals in said books. Catholics were forbidden to read these books without special permission from their local Ordinary.

139. What were Canons 1399 and 2318?

Canon 1399 forbade the publication of various types of books, including those on alleged private revelations, unless they were given permission to be printed/published by the local Ordinary. Canon 2318 concerned the appropriate censures, up to and including excommunication, if the law was broken, though the canon was not specifically related only to book publishing.

140. What was the relationship of Canons 1399 and 2318 to the Index?

Both canons were rooted in the fact that the Index enjoyed the force of law. Without that force, the legality of the two canons was questioned. The CDF responded to this doubt by officially abrogating these canons in PE.[102]

141. Why did Pope Paul VI remove the legal force of the Index of Forbidden Books?

The Roman Dicastery known as the Holy Office—which maintained the Index—was newly constituted by Pope Paul VI and renamed the "Sacred Congregation for the Doctrine of the Faith." The congregation, with its new constitution, was not able to keep up with the sizable amount of writings. This resulted in the decision no longer to update the Index of Forbidden Books.[103] If the Index was no longer being updated, there seemed little use in continuing to allow it the force of ecclesiastical law (see Question 115).[104]

142. Does the discontinuance of the Index of Forbidden Books' "legal force" mean the Index enjoys another type of "force" in the Church?

Yes, PLA stated the Index maintains its "moral force."[105]

143. What does "moral force" mean?

It means the CDF made a distinction between the natural law and the penalties of ecclesiastical law as stated in the Code of Canon Law.

144. What was the distinction?

The meaning of the distinction was to inform the faithful they were still *morally* bound under the natural law not to spread materials contrary to faith and morals, but would no longer receive a penalty under ecclesiastical law if they did spread such materials.

145. Does a person sin if he or she disseminates materials that are or may be contrary to faith and morals?

To contravene *willfully* the moral law in this regard is a sin.[106]

146. Are the faithful permitted to publish books about alleged private revelations without prior censorship?

Under the *moral* law, no they are not permitted to do so as they could be causing grave harm.

147. How, then, will the faithful know if they can disseminate a book or books about alleged private revelations?

Ideally, the faithful will only come into contact with a claim to private revelations after being scrutinized by the local Ordinary. However, the contemporary means of social communication create difficulties for Ordinaries to exercise their right of censorship.[107]

148. Why is this?

The contemporary means of social communication allow for faster and more extensive dissemination of information. Combined with these are the secular notion of intellectual freedom and freedom of the press in western culture. Because of these, local Ordinaries tend to use their right only after much discretion.[108]

149. How can the faithful assist their local Ordinary with respect to censorship and alleged private revelations?

The faithful can assist by exercising virtue and unity with their local Ordinary if they receive word of an alleged revelation, *especially* one that has not undergone censorship.

150. How can the faithful exercise virtue and unity in the above regard?

If a book about an alleged private revelation has not undergone censorship, a proper *sensus fidei* (sense of the faith) informs the Catholic to refrain from the work in question out of obedience to the Church and the moral law.

151. By not reading the work in question, is one not "squelching the Spirit" or "despising prophecy," which is explicitly warned against by St. Paul in 1 Thessalonians 5:19-20?

No. St. Paul said, "Do not extinguish the Spirit, do not despise prophesying, but test everything; hold fast [to] what is good, abstain from every kind of evil."[109] When he says to "*test everything,*" Paul is speaking of the discernment of spirits, which happens *through the Church* so that one "may know how one ought to behave in the household of God, which is the church of the living God, the pillar and foundation of the truth."[110]

152. If the Index is no longer updated, how do the faithful know what books contain matter contrary to faith and morals?

Provision was made in PLA for Ordinaries and conferences of bishops to maintain their own lists of books. The document also states the "mature conscience" of the faithful and the "vigilant solicitude" of the bishops and conferences of bishops are to be utilized as well.

153. What is meant by "mature conscience" and "vigilant solicitude"?

"Mature conscience" means the faithful must be well catechized, properly formed in their consciences, and obedient to the Church and the moral law.[111] "Vigilant solicitude" refers to the duty of local Ordinaries to protect the faith and morals of the flock entrusted to them as well as to instruct them in their moral obligations.[112]

154. Did PLA intend censorship of books by the Church was to be discontinued?

PLA intended for censorship to continue in the Church. The document states bishops, conferences of bishops and Rome itself will "hinder," "censure" and "condemn" harmful books if necessary and that any such judgments on a book will be made known to the faithful.

155. If it was the Church's intention to reform and not abolish ecclesiastical censorship, were there new norms issued on censorship?

After the Second Vatican Council, the CDF released two particular documents treating (either whole or in part) the question of norms on book publishing, censorship and alleged private revelations.

156. What were those two documents?

On March 19, 1975, the CDF issued a decree entitled *Ecclesiae pastorum* (hereafter, EP) on the publication of books in the Church.[113] In December of 1996, the Congregation issued a Press Release (hereafter, PR) in the Vatican's newspaper (*L'Osservatore Romano*) that clarified the legal and moral status of books on alleged private revelations.[114]

157. What did EP say in 1975?

EP provided instructions and canonical norms on the publication of books dealing with the liturgy, the Scriptures, catechisms, diaries, folios, etc. Also included were books treating faith and good morals. None of these books, according to EP, are allowed to be published without the prior censorship of the local Ordinary, conferences of bishops or the Holy See.[115]

158. What did the CDF say in PR?

PR clarified three items of interest for the purposes of this book:

1. Pope Paul VI's reforms of the Church's system of censorship.
2. The role of the bishops of the Church in relation to the censorship of books under the 1983 *Code of Canon Law* (hereafter, 1983 CIC).
3. The juridical character of books on alleged private revelations.

159. Is PR binding upon the Catholic faithful?

PR cites the legally binding canon 823 §1 of the 1983 CIC and interprets books on supposed private revelations as falling under that canon. The CDF's clarification is a part of Catholic law and thus binding upon all the faithful.

160. What did the CDF say in PR about the reforms of Paul VI?

The congregation *explicitly* says, "The interpretation given by some individuals to a Decision approved by Paul VI…in virtue of which writings and messages resulting from alleged revelations could be freely circulated in the Church, is absolutely groundless."[116]

161. What did the CDF say about the role of bishops and censorship?

The congregation encourages bishops to utilize their authority on censorship. It reminds bishops of their canonical right to demand books treating matters of faith and morals be submitted to their judgment before publication.

162. What is the juridical character of books concerning alleged private revelations?

The CDF identifies books on alleged private revelations as books that touch upon faith and morals, and thus Canon 823 §1 of the 1983 CIC (and Canon 654 §2 of the 1990 Code of Canons of the Eastern Churches) is in force.[117]

163. How do books on alleged private revelations undergo censorship?

PR states books go first to the local Ordinary and then progressively (if the situation requires it) to the local conference of bishops and then Rome.[118]

164. How does the process of censorship work?

Dioceses are expected to have available to them a person who is appointed to be the diocesan "censor." Books must first go through the censor, who acts in the name of the bishop. The censor submits his findings to the bishop who issues the final judgment with regards to content and printing.

165. Which bishop does an author go to in order to have his or her book reviewed?

Censorship must be from the author's local Ordinary or the Ordinary of the place where the book(s) is to be published.[119]

166. How does a person know if a book has undergone censorship?

The censor of the diocese reviews the book and, if a favorable review is given, grants a *nihil obstat*. The bishop then receives the manuscript and reviews it and any notes given by the censor. If the bishop finds the work to be in harmony with faith and morals, he grants an "*imprimatur.*"

167. What is the *nihil obstat?*

The *nihil obstat* is a Latin expression meaning "nothing obstructs" publication. Its purpose is to show a book has undergone censorship by the competent Ecclesiastical Authority (usually the local Ordinary) and has been found by the censor to be free from error regarding faith and morals.

168. What is the *imprimatur?*

The *imprimatur* is a Latin expression meaning, "let it be printed." The *imprimatur* is a mark given by a bishop to show he has granted permission for a book to be printed as it has been found not to contain errors in faith and morals.

169. Where can a reader find the *imprimatur* and *nihil obstat* in a book?

Usually, an *imprimatur* and *nihil obstat* can be found within the first few pages of a book. With these is found the name of the bishop (and that of the censor), the dates the *imprimatur* and *nihil obstat* were given and the name of the diocese wherein the *imprimatur* and *nihil obstat* were given.

170. Did Pope Paul VI's reforms to the system of censorship include the dissolution of the *imprimatur* and *nihil obstat*?

Pope Paul VI's reforms to censorship did not include the dissolution of the *imprimatur* and *nihil obstat*.[120]

171. If the *nihil obstat* and *imprimatur* were not dissolved, why do many books on alleged private revelations claim that they are not necessary?

The reason is threefold:

1. Failure to recognize distinctions.
2. Lack of English translations.
3. Improper implementation/catechesis.[121]

172. If there is no legal requirement of the faithful to obtain a *nihil obstat* and *imprimatur*, why would one want to obtain them?

The *nihil obstat* and *imprimatur* help the reader (and author) to know the book can be read with the freedom of mind and heart that comes from knowing one is not endangering his or her eternal salvation.

173. Why is there no specific mandate that any book on alleged private revelations must have an *imprimatur* or *nihil obstat* before the book is published?

Pope Paul VI wanted the *Code* to assist the spiritual life of the faithful as opposed to forcing them with precept.[122] He desired the faithful to fulfill their duties to the moral law of their own volition (and after proper catechetical instruction).

174. If a person publishes a book about alleged private revelations without prior censorship, is he or she acting contrary to Catholic moral teaching?

Objectively, yes, the person *is* acting contrary to Catholic moral teaching.

175. What if someone did not know it was wrong?

The person's level of knowledge must be taken into account as the person may have been misinformed about the facts and acted in good faith based upon his or her understanding of Church teaching at the time of publication.

176. What happens after the person learns he or she ought not to publish books on alleged private revelations without prior censorship?

After being informed of the moral obligations, said person has a duty to cease and desist disseminating any such materials.

177. What if a person is experiencing alleged private revelations but has reason to believe they are diabolical in origin?

In such cases, a technical distinction must be made between knowing *with certainty* and when there is *doubt*.

178. What is the distinction between knowing "with certainty" and having "doubt"?

If anyone possesses certitude he or she is experiencing or aiding diabolical visions or revelations, he or she ought to cease contact with such phenomena. It could be the devil is trying to gain glory for himself by being worshipped under the guise of a heavenly figure. Where there is doubt, "signs of respect should be given *conditionally*."[123]

179. Does the Church provide the faithful with a teaching on any signs of false private revelations to detect a diabolical origin?

The Church's tradition on the interior life of virtue provides the faithful with some general signs to help discern a possible diabolical origin other than those given in Questions 10-11.

180. What are those signs?

According to the Dominican theologian, Dom Reginald Garrigou-Lagrange, the following are to be looked at as signs of the evil spirit:

1. Pride in the soul that leads to trouble, discouragement and even despair.
2. An exaggerated mortification.
3. False humility spurred on by spiritual pride.
4. A focus upon what is most extraordinary and marvelous to make the faithful feel esteemed or bring about what is foreign to our vocation.
5. Presumption, which undermines the theological virtue of hope.
6. The creation of self-love in the faithful.
7. Engendering dissensions and hatreds as opposed to peace.
8. Evident sin which cannot be concealed, creates confusion, vexation and discouragement in the soul.

Fr. Garrigou-Lagrange ends by saying, "the lack of humility and obedience is a certain indication that it is not God who guides [the person in question]."[124]

181. Is it possible the devil would suggest someone to enter religious life or priesthood through alleged private revelations?

It is the *perennial* tradition of the Catholic Church the devil can suggest an individual to enter religious life or priesthood, the question of alleged private revelations notwithstanding.[125]

182. Why would the devil suggest someone enter religious life or become a priest?

The religious state or priesthood could be a means for Satan to tempt a soul to pride or to induce men to other work the devil wishes to do.[126] Alleged private revelations would be a most effective means to accomplish this goal.[127]

183. Should the faithful immediately presume diabolic intervention when people enter the religious state or priesthood vis-à-vis alleged private revelations?

When people enter the religious state or priesthood vis-à-vis alleged private revelations, it is not prudent to presume immediately the devil is suggesting they enter.

184. Why would it not be prudent to presume diabolical intervention?

The Holy Spirit could be the source of the inspiration. Furthermore, as St. Thomas Aquinas teaches, even if the devil indeed was to influence an individual to enter the religious state or priesthood, the attraction ultimately comes from God.[128]

185. It is said the Church looks at the "fruits" produced by alleged private revelations. What does "fruits" mean?

Jesus taught, "[B]y their fruits you shall know them."[129] "Fruits," as understood in the theology of private revelation, mean those virtues or vices that are in the soul and which manifest themselves interiorly or exteriorly in thought, word or deed.

186. What are some examples of good and bad fruits?

Good fruits are those things that encourage people in holiness such as:

1. Increase in one's prayer life.
2. Conversion.
3. Increased docility to the laws and teachings of the Church.
4. Increase in virtue.[130]

Bad fruits lead one away from God. Examples are:

1. Disobedience to the Church and her representatives.
2. Misrepresentation of the Church or her representatives.
3. Increase in pride.

4. Choosing alleged revelations over and above the teaching authority of the Church.

Fr. Garrigou-Lagrange's signs of the evil spirit as given above are also examples of negative fruits. In all things, we would do well to heed the advice of St. Teresa of Avila who wrote:

> Such [mystical] experiences, if we use them aright, prepare us to be better servants of God; but sometimes it is the weakest whom God leads by this road; and so there is no ground here either for approval or for condemnation. We must base our judgments on the virtues. The saintliest will be she who serves Our Lord with the greatest mortification and humility and purity of conscience.[131]

187. Are the fruits the primary focus in the discernment of alleged private revelations?

Not necessarily. NC suggests a local Ordinary start his examination "from the spiritual fruits engendered by the new devotion" and study them in relation to the other criteria. However, it is possible the Ordinary notices immediately an error in faith and morals in an alleged message before looking at any fruits of the devotion.[132] In such cases, it is unnecessary to look at the fruits as an argument toward establishing a supernatural character to the alleged revelations.

188. If the above is true, why are spiritual fruits highly spoken of when discerning alleged private revelations?

This is because Jesus makes them a point of focus in the Gospel as mentioned above. What is necessary is a proper understanding of what fruits are and are not as well as how to detect legitimate from illegitimate fruits, including good ones from rotten ones.[133] This detection takes time and is a part of the discernment process.[134]

189. Is it possible good fruits may not necessarily come from alleged private revelations such as an apparition or locution?

Yes, spiritual good fruits might not have their origin in alleged private revelations or similar phenomena.

190. What could be the origin of apparent good fruits attributed to alleged private revelations?

Jesus says in the Gospel, "Where two or three are gathered in my name, there am I in the midst of them."[135] It is possible for any apparent good fruit to be a result of the community of the faithful gathered together in unity in the name of Jesus Christ.[136]

191. Does the fact of the faithful being in a place because of alleged private revelations have any relevance to the good fruit?

No, the original reason for the gathering does not have any bearing upon the fact of grace coming from where two or three are gathered in the name of Jesus Christ.

192. Would it be presumptuous to attribute immediately a conversion or any other good fruit to alleged private revelations?

Yes, an immediate attribution of apparent good fruit to alleged private revelations—especially in the form of alleged messages—would be presumptuous, though this may vary from case to case as the facts merit.

193. Why would it be presumptuous?

"Prudence is the virtue that disposes practical reason to discern our true good in every circumstance and to choose the right means of achieving it."[137] Prudence would seek whether or not the alleged revelations are for our true good and the best means to achieve that good.[138] It would not be in keeping with prudence to accept immediately any claims to heavenly messages at face value without investigation and critical thought. The Church looks at *all* the fruits, not just some "good" ones because one rotten fruit can spoil the rest.

194. Should the faithful be desirous to receive private revelations?

The faithful should not be desirous to receive private revelations.

195. Why not?

The faithful should not be desirous to receive private revelations because "such behavior is neither good, nor pleasing to God. Rather he is displeased; not only displeased but frequently angered and deeply offended."[139] St. Teresa of Avila also states, "I will only warn you that, when you learn or hear that God is granting souls these graces, you must never beseech or desire Him to lead you along this road."[140]

196. Why would God be displeased and deeply offended?

The reason for God's displeasure for such inordinate searching rests upon the fact God has created us within certain limits that may not be transgressed. St. John of the Cross says:

> No creature may licitly go beyond the boundaries naturally ordained by God for its governance. He has fixed natural and rational limits by which humans are to be ruled. A desire to transcend them, hence, is unlawful, and to desire to investigate and arrive at knowledge in a supernatural way is to go beyond the natural limits. It is unlawful, consequently, and God who is offended by everything illicit is displeased.[141]

197. If people ask for such private revelations, would God grant the request?

Yes, it is possible that God may grant the request.

198. Why would God grant the request if it displeases Him?

St. John of the Cross teaches:

> Sometimes the devil answers; but when God answers, he does so because of the weakness of the individual who desires to advance in that way. Such persons could become sad and turn back, or imagine that God is unhappy with them, and become over-whelmed. Or there may be other motives known to God, prompted by the weaknesses of these persons. And, as a result, God sees the appropriateness of condescending with such an answer….But he does not act thus because he is desirous or pleased that communication with him be carried on in such a manner.[142]

199. If a person displeases God by such a request, is he or she sinning?

St. John of the Cross held:

> …a person who tries to get knowledge in this supernatural way—as well as the one who commands this or gives consent—[cannot] help but sin, at least venially, no matter how excellent the motives or advanced in perfection that person may be.[143]

200. Would God permit widespread confusion about a claim to alleged private revelations?

Yes, God would permit such confusion to happen.

201. Why would God allow such confusion?

According to St. John of the Cross:

> God permits the devil to blind and delude many who

> merit this [blindness and delusion] by their sins and audacities. The devil is able and successful to the extent that others believe what he says and consider him a good spirit. So firm is their belief that it is impossible for anyone who tries to persuade them of the diabolic origin. For with God's permission they have already been affected by the spirit of misunderstanding.[144]

Thus we see Holy Mother Church has carefully provided her faithful children (whether they receive private revelations or not) with the means to discern alleged private revelations. She has established norms for claims of private revelation to be discerned by the competent Ecclesiastical Authority and the faithful are expected to follow these norms of discernment as well as obey the directives issued by said Authority on private revelation.

The following section is the Appendices. The documents contained therein either directly concern private revelation or affect this subject. They are provided for the reader to peruse at his or her leisure and to gain a greater appreciation for the magisterial teaching on the subject.

—APPENDIX A—

Letter *Normae S. Congregationis*
Congregation for the Doctrine of the Faith,
February, 1978

Norms Regarding the Manner of Proceeding in the Discernment of Presumed Apparitions or Revelations[145]

Preliminary Note
Origin and character of these norms

During the annual Plenary Session in November 1974, the Fathers of this Sacred Congregation examined the problems relative to presumed apparitions and to the revelations often connected with them and reached the following conclusions:

1. Today, more than in the past, news of these apparitions is diffused rapidly among the faithful thanks to the means of information (*mass media*). Moreover, the ease of going from one place to another fosters frequent pilgrimages, so that Ecclesiastical Authority should discern quickly about the merits of such matters.
2. On the other hand, modern mentality and the require-

> ments of critical scientific investigation render it more difficult, if not almost impossible, to achieve with the required speed the judgments that in the past concluded the investigation of such matters (*constat de supernaturalitate, non constat de supernaturalitate*) and that offered to the Ordinaries the possibility of authorizing or prohibiting public cult or other forms of devotion among the faithful.

For these reasons, in order that the devotion stirred among the faithful as a result of facts of this sort might manifest itself in full communion with the Church, and bear fruits by which the Church herself might later discern the true nature of the facts, the Fathers judged that in this matter the following procedure should be promoted.

When Ecclesiastical Authority is informed of a presumed apparition or revelation, it will be its responsibility:

a. first, to judge the fact according to positive and negative criteria (cf. *infra*, no. I);
b. then, if this examination results in a favorable conclusion, to permit some public manifestation of cult or of devotion, overseeing this with great prudence (equivalent to the formula, "for now, nothing stands in the way") (*pro nunc nihil obstare*).
c. finally, in light of time passed and of experience, with special regard to the fecundity of spiritual fruit generated from this new devotion, to express a judgment regarding the authenticity and supernatural character if the case so merits.

I. Criteria for Judging, at Least With Probability, the Character of the Presumed Apparitions or Revelations

A) Positive Criteria:

a. Moral certitude, or at least great probability of the existence of the fact, acquired by means of a serious investigation;
b. Particular circumstances relative to the existence and to the nature of the fact, that is to say:
    1. Personal qualities of the subject or of the subjects (in particular, psychological equilibrium, honesty and rectitude of moral life, sincerity and habitual docility towards Ecclesiastical Authority, the capacity to return to a normal regimen of a life of faith, etc.);
    2. As regards revelation: true theological and spiritual doctrine and immune from error;
    3. Healthy devotion and abundant and constant spiritual fruit (for example, spirit of prayer, conversion, testimonies of charity, etc.).

B) Negative Criteria:

a. Manifest error concerning the fact.
b. Doctrinal errors attributed to God Himself, or to the Blessed Virgin Mary, or to some saint in their manifestations, taking into account however the possibility that the subject might have added, even unconsciously, purely human elements or some error of the natural order to an authentic supernatural revelation (cf. Saint Ignatius, *Exercises*, no. 336).
c. Evidence of a search for profit or gain strictly connected to the fact.
d. Gravely immoral acts committed by the subject or his or her followers when the fact occurred or in connection with it.

e. Psychological disorder or psychopathic tendencies in the subject, that with certainty influenced on the presumed supernatural fact, or psychosis, collective hysteria or other things of this kind.

It is to be noted that these criteria, be they positive or negative, are not peremptory but rather indicative, and they should be applied cumulatively or with some mutual convergence.

II. Intervention of the competent ecclesiastical authority

1. If, on the occasion of a presumed supernatural fact, there arises in a spontaneous way among the faithful a certain cult or some devotion, the competent Ecclesiastical Authority has the serious duty of looking into it without delay and of diligently watching over it.
2. If the faithful request it legitimately (that is, in communion with the Pastors, and not prompted by a sectarian spirit), the competent Ecclesiastical Authority can intervene to permit or promote some form of cult or devotion, if, after the application of the above criteria, nothing stands in the way. They must be careful that the faithful not interpret this practice as approval of the supernatural nature of the fact on the part of the Church (cf. Preliminary note c).
3. By reason of its doctrinal and pastoral task, the competent Authority can intervene *motu proprio* and indeed must do so in grave circumstances, for example in order to correct or prevent abuses in the exercise of cult and devotion, to condemn erroneous doctrine, to avoid the dangers of a false or unseemly mysticism, etc.
4. In doubtful cases that clearly do not put the good of the Church at risk, the competent Ecclesiastical Authority is

to refrain from any judgment and from any direct action (because it can also happen that, after a certain period of time, the presumed supernatural fact falls into oblivion); it must not however cease from being vigilant by intervening if necessary, with promptness and prudence.

III. Authorities Competent to Intervene

1. Above all, the duty of vigilance and intervention falls to the Ordinary of the place.
2. The regional or national Conference of Bishops can intervene:
   a. If the Ordinary of the place, having done his part, turns to it to judge the matter with greater certainty;
   b. If the matter pertains to the national or regional level; always, however, with the prior consent of the Ordinary of the place.
3. The Apostolic See can intervene if asked either by the Ordinary himself, by a qualified group of the faithful, or even directly by reason of the universal jurisdiction of the Supreme Pontiff (cf. *infra*, no. IV).

IV. On the Intervention of the Sacred Congregation for the Doctrine of the Faith

1. a) The intervention of the Sacred Congregation can be requested either by the Ordinary, after he has done his part, or by a qualified group of the faithful. In this second case, care must be taken that recourse to the Sacred Congregation not be motivated by suspect reasons (for example, in order to compel the Ordinary to modify his own legit-

imate decisions, to support some sectarian group, etc.).

b) It is up to the Sacred Congregation to intervene *motu proprio* in graver cases, especially if the matter affects the larger part of the Church, always after having consulted the Ordinary and even, if the situation requires, the Conference of Bishops.

2. It is up to the Sacred Congregation to judge and approve the Ordinary's way of proceeding or, in so far as it be possible and fitting, to initiate a new examination of the matter, distinct from that undertaken by the Ordinary and carried out either by the Sacred Congregation itself or by a special Commission.

The Present Norms, deliberated in the Plenary Session of this Sacred Congregation, were approved by the Supreme Pontiff, Paul VI on 24 February 1978.

In Rome, from the palace of the Sacred Congregation for the Doctrine of the Faith, 25 February 1978.

Francis Cardinal Šeper
Prefect

Jérôme Hamer, O.P.
Secretary

—APPENDIX B—

Bull *Sanctissimus Dominus Noster*
Pope Urban VIII, March 13, 1625

Introduction:

Sanctissimus Dominus Noster (*Sanctissimus*) and its later counterpart, *Coelestis Hierusalem* (*Coelestis*) are foundational documents in the history of beatifications and canonizations, and should be understood in that context.[146] For the purposes of this book, these two Bulls are important because they contain matter that touches upon the subject of private revelation in relation to Pope Urban VIII. These Bulls reveal Urban VIII said more about the subject than that which he is often credited vis-à-vis the alleged "it is better to believe" quote.

Sanctissimus and *Coelestis* were written to stop abuses in the Church concerning devotion that arose around people who were reputed to have died in sanctity. The abuse was the painting of images of said persons with halos, laurels and rays and placing them in churches and other public places. Purported miracles and revelations attributed to said persons were also circulating in written form among the faithful. These were considered an abuse because said persons were not beatified or canonized by Rome, and acting as though the deceased was canonized or beatified created a moral problem. Pope Urban acted to preserve the integrity of faith and morals.

Especially from the Council of Trent onwards, miracles, revelations, visions, relics, paintings, etc., were all seen as "pious traditions." This is why, almost 400 years later, Pope St. Pius X in his Encyclical *Pascendi Dominici Gregis* (*Pascendi*) employs the term "pious traditions" (paragraph 55). St. Pius X takes his terminology and understanding directly from the tradition, of which *Sanctissimus* is a part. In *Pascendi*, Pius X orders Urban's decree to be upheld in those books on pious traditions that have ecclesiastical approval.[147] Strangely enough, the opposite has happened in recent years.

The Church has clear and consistent papal teaching on what is called "pious traditions." That teaching states no book may be published about revelations, miracles, etc., without ecclesiastical approval. In our day, a vast number of the faithful understands Pope Urban VIII only in terms of the alleged "it is better to believe" quote. The reasons for this are a matter for historical conjecture.

Sanctissimus seems to conflict with the "it is better to believe" statement. Further thought, however, would rule out such a conclusion because a person can privately believe in an alleged private revelation (unless the competent Ecclesiastical Authority has ruled otherwise) but they cannot publish a book or books on it without ecclesiastical permission. Though *Sanctissimus* does not answer the question of whether or not Urban really said "it is better to believe," it does help Catholics to understand better the person and teachings of Pope Urban VIII. If he did make the quote, it must be understood in harmony with what Urban promulgated on and publicly stated about alleged private revelations.

Following the text of *Sanctissimus* is an accompanying document provided in the Taurinensis Edition of *Bullarum Romanum* called "*Postmodum vero*" (hereafter, PV).[148] It is here reproduced and is considered by this author a part of *Sanctissimus*. PV was a later document that answered a question as to whether or not churches, oratories or public/private places were allowed to receive objects about persons said to be holy but without displaying them for the faithful.

The Latin texts of *Sanctissimus* and PV are provided with an accompanying English translation. The translation of *Sanctissimus* and PV is the work of Dr. Michael Woodward.

Sanctissimus Dominus Noster
Bull of Pope Urban VIII, March 13, 1625
Bullarum Romanum, Taurinensis Edition, 1868, 809-811.

Latin Text:

CXXX

Prohibet, quominus imagines nondum a Sede Apostolica canonizatorum, vel beatificorum, cum radiis, splendoribus et laureolis proponantur, vel tabellae et luminaria ad eorum sepulchra apponantur, etc.

Feria v, die XIII martii, anno a Nativitate Domini Nostri Iesu Christi MDCXXV, in generali Congregatione S. Romanae e universalis Inquisitionis habita in palatio apostolico in Vaticano coram SS. D. N. D. Urbano divina providentia Papa VIII, ac illustrissimis et reverendissimis DD. S. R. E. cardinalibus adversus haereticam pravitatem inquisitoribus generalibus a sancta Sede Apostolica specialiter deputatis.

SANCTISSIMUS D.N. sollicite animadvertens abusus, qui irrepserunt et quotidie irrepere non cessant in colendis quibusdam cum sanctitatis aut martyrii fama vel opinione defunctis, qui, etsi neque canonizationis, neque beatificationis honore insigniti sint ab Apostolica Sede, eorum tamen imagines in oratoriis, atque ecclesiis, aliisque locis publicis, ac etiam privatis, cum laureolis, aut radiis, seu splendoribus proponuntur, miracula et revelationes, aliaque beneficia a Deum per eorum intercessiones accepta, in libris rerum ab ipsis gestarum enarrantur, et ad illorum sepulchra tabellae, imagines et res aliae ad beneficia accepta testificanda et lampades et alia lumina apponuntur,

Prohibet, ne imagines nondum beatificatorum cum aureolis exponantur.

§1. Volensque proinde huiusmodi abusibus, pro debito officii pastoralis, occurrere, re etiam cum illustrissimis et reverendissimis DD. cardinalibus contra haereticam pravitatem in universa republica christiana generalibus inquisitoribus communicata, et mature considerata ac discussa, declaravit, statuit et decrevit, ne quorumvis hominum cum sanctitatis seu martyrii fama (quantacumque illa sit) defunctorum imagines, aliaque praedicta, et quodcumque aliud venerationem et cultum praeseferens et indicans, in oratoriis, aut locis publicis seu privatis, vel ecclesiis, tam secularibus quam regularibus, cuiuscumque religionis, ordinis, instituti, congregationis, aut societatis, apponantur, antequam ab Apostolica Sede canonizentur, aut Beati declarentur, et si quae appositae sunt, amoveantur, prout eas statim amoveri mandavit.

Vel eorum gesta typis publicentur sine licentia.

§2. Ac partier imprimi de cetero inhibuit libros eorumdem hominum, qui sanctitatis, sive martyrii fama, vel opinione, ut praefertur, celebres e vita migraverint, gesta, miracula vel revelationes, seu quaecumque beneficia tamquam eorum intercessionibus a Deo accepta continentes, sine recognitione atque approbatione Ordinarii, qui in iis recognoscendis theologos, aliosque pios ac doctos viros in consilium adhibeat; et, ne deinceps fraus, aut error, aut aliquid novum ac inordinatum in re tam gravi committatur, negotium instructum ad Sedem Apostolicam transmittat, eiusque responsum expectet. Revelationes vero et miracula, aliaque beneficia supradicta, quae in libris horum hominum vitam et gesta continentibus hactenus sine recognitione atque approbatione huiusmodi impressa sunt, nullo modo approbata censeri vult, mandatque Sua Sanctitas.

Aut ad eorum sepulchra tabellae, aut lampades ponantur.

§3. Ad horum hominum sepulchra vetuit etiam ac inhibuit tabellas atque imagines ex cera aut argento seu ex alia quacumque materia tam pictas quam fictas atque exculptas appendi aut affigi, et lampades sive alia quaecumque lumina accendi, sine recognitione ab Ordinario omnino, prout supra, facienda, Sedique apostolicae referenda ac probanda.

Excepiuntur ii, quibus favet cultus immemorabilis.

§4. Declarans, quod per suprascripta praeiudicare in aliquo non vult neque intendit iis, qui aut per communem Ecclesiae consensum, vel immemorabilem temporis cursum, aut per Patrum, virorumque sanctorum scripta, vel longissimi temporis, scientia ac tolerantia Sedis Apostolicae, vel Ordinarii, coluntur.

Ordinariis locorum executionem demandat.

§5. Ut autem praemissa diligentius observentur, universis, ac singulis, tam Ordinariis quam haereticae pravitatis inquisitoribus, districte praecipit, ut in sua quisque dioecesi vel provincia sedulo pervigilent, ne sine approbationibus praedictis imagines cum memoratis signis exponantur, aut miracula, revelationes ac beneficia praedicta publicentur, aliave contra superius disposita fiant.

Poenas transgressoribus infligit.

§6. Transgressores vero, si regulares fuerint, privationis suorum officiorum, ac vocis activae et passivae, necnon et suspensionis a divinis; si vero clerici seculars, privationis pariter suorum officiorum, suspensionis a divinis et ab administratione sacramentorum, exequutioneque suorum ordinum respective, aliisque arbitrio praedictorum Ordinariorum seu inquisitorum, pro modo culpae, infligendis poenis plectendo.

Praesentium publication.

§7. Qui autem libros impresserint, aut imagines pinxerint, sculpserint, seu quoquomodo effinxerint, vel formaverint, ceterique artifices, circa praemissa qualitercumque delinquentes, praedicta omnia amittant et insuper pecuniariis aliisque etiam corporalibus poenis, iuxta criminis gravitatem, eorumdem Ordinariorum seu inquisitorum arbitrio afficiantur.

§8. Contrariis quibuscumque non obstantibus.

Transumptis danda fides.

§9. Et ne praemissorum ignorantia possit ab aliquo praetendi, voluit, ut decretum huiusmodi, seu illius exemplum, ad valvas basilicae Principis apostolorum Urbis ac in acie Campi Florae affixum omnes perinde arctet atque afficiat, ac si unicuique personaliter intimatum fuisset.

§10. Quodque praesentium transumptis, etiam impressis, manu notarii publici subscriptis, ac sigillo alicuius personae in dignitate ecclesiastica constitutae munitis, eadem prorsus fides habeatur, quae praesentibus adhiberetur, si forent exhibitae, vel ostensae.

IOANNES ANTONIUS THOMASIUS,
S. Romanae et universalis Inquisit. not.

Anno MDCXXV, indictione VII, pontificatus Sanctissimi Domini nostri Domini Urbani divina providentia Papae VIII anno eius secundo, die vero quarta mensis aprilis, supradictum decretum affixum et publicatum fuit ad valvas basilicae Principis apostolorum de Urbe, et in acie Campi Florae, ut moris est, per me Brandimartem Latinum, Sanctissimi Domini nostri Papae cursorem.

OCTAVIUS SPADA,
magister cursorum.

Sequitur declaratio praeinsertae prohibitionis

POSTMODUM VERO idem Sanctissimus Dominus noster a quibusdam revocari in dubium accepit, an tabellas et imagines, quas in posterum offerri contigerit, recipere, et antea oblatas conservare liceret. Sanctitas Sua, quae tantummodo voluit, occurrendo abusibus qui irrepere videbantur, certiorem parare viam ad eorum in terris gloriam, quorum sanctimoniam divinae clementiae placuerit admirandis operibus illustrare, re prius cum illustrissimis et reverendissimis DD. cardinalibus contra haereticam pravitatem generalibus inquisitoribus communicata, praesenti decreto declaravit: Quod, sicut nunquam prohibuit, nec suae intentionis fuit prohibere oblationem, receptionemque tabellarum et imaginum huiusmodi, ita, ut nulli deinceps haesitationi locus relinquatur, statuit in praesentiarum et decernit, ut quoties ad aliquam ecclesiam, aut oratorium, locumve alium publicum, secularem seu regularem, tabellas et imagines, aliudve simile quisquam detulerit, ac intercessione hominum inter Sanctos vel Beatos non adscriptorum, quamvis cum martyrii vel sanctitatis fama demortuorum, optata se impetravisse dixerit, liceat ecclesiasticis personis, ecclesiarum, locorumve praedictorum curae praepositis, tabellas et imagines, sive pictas, sive ex quavis materia fictas, atque alia quaecumque collatae gratiae fidem facientia, simul cum deferentis, aliorumque, qui conscii fuerint, attestationibus, accipere, atque approbantibus Ordinariis, ad quos referre statim omnia teneantur, in secreto aliquo, seorsum ab ecclesia, loco custodire, ibidemque iam amota collocare et asservare, ut, si quando Dominus talium virorum merita beatificationis seu canonizationis honore in terris decorare voluerit, extent huiusmodi sanctitatis qualescumque probationes, Apostolicae Sedis iudicio tunc examinandae. Contrariis quibuscumque non obstantibus.

IOANNES ANTONIUS THOMASIUS
S. Romanae et universalis Inquisit. not.

English Translation:

CXXX

Prohibits images of those not yet canonized or beatified by the Apostolic See from being displayed with rays, halos, and laurels, or pictures and lamps from being placed at their tombs, etc.

On Thursday, the 13th day of March, in the year of the Nativity of Our Lord Jesus Christ 1625, in the general meeting of the Holy Roman and universal Inquisition, held at the apostolic palace in the Vatican in the presence of the most holy lord, by divine providence our lord Pope Urban VIII, and of the most illustrious and most reverend Cardinals, lords of the Holy Roman Church, specially appointed by the holy Apostolic See as inquisitor generals against heretical depravity.

OUR MOST HOLY LORD [Pope Urban], has directed his attention to abuses that have crept in and do not cease from creeping in daily with the honoring of certain people who died with the reputation or rumor of sanctity or martyrdom. For although they have not been honored by the Apostolic See with the tribute of canonization or beatification, nevertheless their images are displayed with laurels, rays, or halos in oratories, churches, and other public places, and even in private homes. Miracles, revelations, and other benefits received from God through their intercession are recounted in books of their deeds. Pictures, images, and other things testifying to the benefits received, and torches and other lamps are placed at their tombs.

1. Wishing, then, to counter such abuses, according to the duty of his pastoral office, and with the matter brought up in council and maturely considered and discussed by the most illustrious and reverend lord Cardinals, inquisitor generals against heretical depravity in the whole Christian republic, our Holy Father declared, established, and decreed, that the images, and other aforementioned things, of any men who died with the reputation, however great, of sanctity or martyrdom, and anything else that presents or indicates veneration or worship, are not to be placed in oratories, public or private places, churches, both secular and regular, of whatever religion, order, institute, congregation, or society before they are canonized or declared blessed by the Apostolic See; and if any have been so placed, they should be removed, since he ordered them to be removed immediately.
2. Similarly, and first among other matters, he prohibited books about those people, who were famous when they left this life with a reputation or rumor of sanctity or martyrdom, containing the deeds, miracles, revelations, or whatever benefits received from God as through their intercessions, without the recognition and approval of the Ordinary, who, in giving recognition to them, should call into council theologians and other pious and learned men. And lest, after this, fraud or error or anything novel and inordinate be committed in so grave a matter, let the Or-

dinary deliver the documented affair to the Apostolic See and wait for its response. His Holiness, moreover, wills and commands that the revelations, miracles, and other benefits related above, which are printed in books containing the life and deeds of those people, and so far without the stated recognition and approval, should in no way be considered approved.

3. He also forbade and prohibited pictures and images of wax, silver, or any other material, whether painted, molded, or sculpted, from being hung or attached to the tombs of these people, and torches or any other lamps from being lit, without the full recognition that must be given, as related above, by the Ordinary and referred and approved by the Apostolic See.
4. He also declared that he does not wish or intend the above to be in any way prejudicial toward those who are honored by the common consent of the Church, or by the course of time immemorial, or by the writings of the Fathers and other holy men, or with the long-standing knowledge and toleration of the Apostolic See or the Ordinary.
5. In order, additionally, that the foregoing be more diligently observed, he strictly commands each and every Ordinary and inquisitor of heretical depravity to keep careful watch in his own diocese or province lest, without the said approvals, images with the mentioned figures be displayed, or the mentioned miracles, revelations, and benefits be published, or any other things be done against what has been set forth above.
6. Now transgressors, if they are regular clerics, shall be punished by the removal of their offices, of both active or passive voice, and also the suspension from divine duties; and if they are secular clerics, by the removal from their offices as well, the suspension from divine duties,

from the administration of the Sacraments, from the performance of their respective orders, and by other punishments to be inflicted, in the judgment of the said Ordinaries and inquisitors, according to the circumstances of the violation.

7. And those who print books, or who paint, sculpt, or in any way fashion or form images, and other artisans who transgress howsoever as mentioned, shall lose all these works, and be afflicted further with any monetary and other punishments, even corporal, in the judgment of their Ordinaries or inquisitors, according to the gravity of the crime.
8. With all things to the contrary notwithstanding.
9. And lest anyone be able to pretend ignorance of the foregoing, he willed that this decree or a copy of it, having been affixed to the doors of the basilica of the City of the Prince of the Apostles, and at the corner of Campo dei Fiori, shall bind and bear upon all equally, as if each one had been warned in person.
10. The words of those present were recorded, printed, and subscribed in the hand of the notary public and confirmed with the seal of a person placed in ecclesiastical dignity; and the same confidence, credited to them by those present, should fully apply when they are exhibited or displayed.

Ioannes Antonius Thomasius,
Notary of the Holy Roman and Universal Inquisition

In the year 1625, in the 7th indiction, in the second year of the pontificate of the most holy lord, by divine providence our lord Pope Urban VIII, and on the 4th day of the month of April, the above decree was published and affixed to the doors of the basilica in the city of the Prince of the Apostles, and at the corner of Campo dei Fiore, as is customary, by me, Brandimars Latinus, courier of our most holy lord Pope.

Octavius Spada,
master courier

The declaration of the above prohibition follows:

LATER our Most Holy Lord [Pope Urban] agreed to handle a question of certain people, whether they are allowed to receive pictures and images that come to be offered for the future and to keep them before they are offered. His Holiness, who, in countering the abuses that were seen to be creeping in, only wished to provide a more certain way to the praise on earth of those whose sanctity by divine mercy God is pleased to illustrate in marvelous works. In terms of the matter previously discussed with the most illustrious and most reverend lord cardinals, general inquisitors against heretical depravity, by the present decree he declared that, just as he never prohibited, nor was it his intention to prohibit, the offering and reception of such pictures and images, therefore, in order that henceforth no place be left for any hesitation, he established here and decreed that whenever anyone shall bring pictures and images, or anything similar, to any church, oratory, or other public place, secular or regular, and shall say that he had obtained what he desired through the intercession of those who are not counted among the Saints and Blesseds, although they died with the reputation of martyrdom or holiness, it is lawful for the said ecclesiastical persons in the churches or other mentioned places in their care, to receive pictures and images, painted or fashioned from any material, and other things, whatsoever gives confirmation of the conferred favor, together with the testimonies of the donator and of others who are associates, and to keep them for the approving Ordinaries, to whom they are bound to report all things immediately, and to guard them in some hidden place apart from the church, and therein to gather and preserve the things now removed so that, if and when the Lord should wish to adorn on earth the merits of such men with the honor of beatification or canonization, such proofs of their sanctity remains, to be examined at that time by the judgment of the Apostolic See. With all things to the contrary not withstanding.

Ioannes Antonius Thomasius
Notary of the Holy Roman and Universal Inquisition

In the year 1625, in the 7th indiction, of the pontificate of our most holy lord, by divine providence Lord Pope Urban VIII, on the 30th day of the month of October, the above letter or decree was published and affixed to the doors of the City of the Prince of the Apostles, and at the corner of Campo dei Fiore, as is customary, by me, Brandimars Latinus, courier of our most holy lord Pope.

—APPENDIX C—

Notification *Post Litteras Apostolicas*
Congregation for the Doctrine of the Faith
June 14, 1966

Introduction:

A significant part of the Church's discernment of alleged private revelations concerns the content regarding faith and morals in the writings being reviewed. Since the end of the Council of Trent, the Catholic Church kept a list of condemned books called The Index of Forbidden Books precisely for the purpose of safeguarding faith and morals. An entire Sacred Congregation of the Index was created in the Roman Curia for this purpose and was later merged with the Holy Office by Pope Benedict XV, becoming the "Section for the Index". The Index's last edition was published in 1948.

Before and during the Second Vatican Council, there were some remarks made against the Index of Forbidden Books.[149] Public opposition to the Index was no secret and hopes were raised shortly after the Council closed on December 8, 1965. In early February of 1966, the new *Annuario Pontificio* (Pontifical Yearbook) for 1966 was published. This book contains materials such as phone numbers, Vatican departments and their heads, etc. In American newspapers, it was noted that the "Section for the Index" was omitted from the *Annuario*.[150] This omission raised questions as to the future of the Index.

Two months later on April 24, 1966, Cardinal Ottaviani responded to several questions in the Italian publication L'*Osservatore della Domenica*. The Cardinal wrote to clarify what was happening with the Index. Though the article did receive some press in the United States, the article itself was in Italian. Thus, many American Catholics did not have access to the article in its entirety, to say nothing of an English translation. It was not until 1968 that even the Vatican's newspaper L'*Osservatore Romano* became available in English.

In the L'*Osservatore della Domenica* article, Cardinal Ottaviani specifically states that in the climate of the Church after Vatican II, the Church would rather use admonishments and warnings than condemn writings (unless absolutely necessary). Cardinal Ottaviani further stated there was an "absolute lack of organization" (with respect to updating the Index) that the newly organized Congregation had inherited with respect to contemporary literature. In short, it was not possible for the Congregation to keep up and Cardinal Ottaviani indicated there would be a change in the Index's condition.[154]

On June 14, 1966, Cardinal Ottaviani issued a *Notification* entitled *Post Litteras Apostolicas* (PLA) that declared the Index no longer had *legal* force but only *moral* force. This was a technical change and one that required more work and responsibility on the part of the faithful, the local ordinaries and the conferences of bishops. The CDF stated in PLA, "the Church relies on the *mature conscience of the faithful*" and she "places the *firmest confidence* in the *vigilant solicitude* of all Ordinaries and of the Conference of Bishops" (Emphases mine).

Some Catholics interpreted the news of the Index (and the

soon-to-be-abrogated canons) as the means by which alleged private revelations could be freely spread. This hypothesis was explicitly answered by the Vatican in 1996 and it remains to implement appropriately the documents in the larger Catholic ethos. Providing the documents in question is an important step of that implementation.

The translation of *Post Litteras Apostolicas* was done by Dr. Michael Woodward.

Latin Text:
Acta Apostolicae Sedis, Volume 58, 1966, page 445:

ACTA
SS. Congregationum Sacra Congregatio pro Doctrina Fidei

NOTIFICATIO

POST LITTERAS APOSTOLICAS, a verbis incipientes <<Integrae servandae>> Motu Proprio datae die VII mensis decembris anno 1965, non paucae pervenerunt ad S. Sedem percontationes de Indicis librorum prohibitorum conditione, quo Ecclesia ad integritatem fidei et morum, iuxta divinum mandatum, tuendam hucusque usa est.

Ut memoratis petitionibus respondeatur, haec S. Congregatio pro Doctrina Fidei, facto verbo cum Beatissimo Patre, nuntiat Indicem suum vigorem moralem servare, quatenus Christifidelium conscientiam docet, ut ab illis scriptis, ipso iure naturali exigente, caveant, quae fidem ac bonos mores in discrimen adducere possint; eundem tamen non amplius vim legis ecclesiasticae habere cum adiectis censuris.

Quam ob rem Ecclesia fidelium maturae conscientiae confidit, praesertim auctorum et editorum catholicorum atque eorum qui iuvenibus instituendis operam navant. Firmissimam autem spem collocat in vigili sollicitudine et singulorum Ordinariorum et Conferentiarum Episcopalium, quorum ius et officium est libros noxios tum inspiciendi tum praeveniendi atque, si res tulerit, reprehendendi et improbandi.

S. Congregatio pro Doctrina Fidei, ad mentem Litterarum Apostolicarum <<Integrae servandae>> ac Concilii Vaticani II decretorum, communicare sataget, si opus est, cum orbis catholici Ordinariis ut eorum sedulitatem adiuvet, in diiudicandis operibus editis, in sana contra insidiosam promovenda cultura, collatis etiam viribus cum Institutis et studiorum Universitatibus.

Si autem doctrinae et opiniones quovis modo evulgatae prodierint, quae fidei ac morum principiis adversentur, et eorum auctores ad errores corrigendos humaniter invitati id facere noluerint, S. Sedes iure et officio suo utetur ad talia scripta etiam publice reprobanda, ut animarum bono ea qua par est firmitate consulat.

Apte denique providebitur, ut Ecclesiae iudicium de editis operibus in Christifidelium notitiam perveniat.

Datum Romae, ex Aedibus S. Officii, d. XIV iunii, a. MCMLXVI.

A. Card. Ottaviani,
Pro-Praefectus S. C. pro Doctrina Fidei
+ P. Parente, *a Secretis*

English Translation:

ACTS
of the Sacred Congregation for the Doctrine of the Faith

Notification

AFTER THE APOSTOLIC LETTER that begins with the

words *Integrae servandae*, given by Motu Proprio on the 7th day of the month of December in the year 1965, many inquiries have reached the Holy See concerning the status of the Index of Forbidden Books, by which, according to divine command, the Church up till now has been accustomed to safeguard the integrity of faith and morals.

In order to respond to these petitions, this Sacred Congregation for the Doctrine of the Faith, in agreement with our most blessed Father, declares that the Index maintains its moral force insofar as it instructs the conscience of the Christian faithful, so that, as the natural law itself requires, they may be warned away from those writings which put faith and good morals at risk; nevertheless, it no longer has the power of ecclesiastical law with its corresponding censures.

Therefore the Church relies on the mature conscience of the faithful, especially Catholic authors and publishers and those who undertake the work of educating young people. Moreover she places the firmest confidence in the vigilant solicitude of all Ordinaries and of the Conferences of Bishops, whose right and duty it is both to inspect and to hinder harmful books and, if the matter warrants, to censure and condemn them.

The Sacred Congregation for the Doctrine of the Faith, according to the intention of the Apostolic Letter *Integrae servandae* and of the decrees of the Second Vatican Council, shall be diligent in holding discussions, if necessary, with the Ordinaries of the Catholic world in order to assist their vigilance in judging published works, in promoting a sound culture against an insidious one, and in uniting their powers with educational institutes and universities.

If, however, doctrines and opinions appear in public which oppose the principles of faith and morals, or if their authors, having been gently called upon to correct their errors, are unwilling to do so, the Holy See shall make use of its right and duty to reprove such writings publicly, so that it may look after the good of souls with proper firmness.

Finally, it shall be rightly provided that the Church's judgment concerning published works come to the awareness of the Christian faithful.

Given at Rome from the Palace of the Holy Office, on the 14 day of June, in the year 1966.

A. Cardinal Ottaviani,
Pro-Prefect, S. C. for the Doctrine of the Faith

+ P. Parente, *Secretary*

—APPENDIX D—

Article *Le nuove disposizioni*
Congregation for the Doctrine of the Faith
June 15, 1966

Introduction:

On June 15, 1966, the Vatican's newspaper L'*Osservatore Romano* officially published PLA on the change in the condition of the Index of Forbidden Books.[155] PLA would be placed later in the official journal of the Holy See, the *Acta Apostolicae Sedis*. What is of interest is the article that accompanied PLA as it interprets the document.

The article begins with a historical outline starting with how the Church received a divine mandate from her founder to realize the reign of God in the world for the salvation of all. It then discusses how, over time, the Church struggled against various errors to faith and morals and then goes into how the Index came to be. The article traces the Index back to the invention of the printing press and then recognizes that the system of the Index was useful but inadequate in the long run.

The article goes on to reference Pope Paul VI's awareness of the situation of the Church in the contemporary world. Part of his way of handling the changed situation was restructuring (or "renovating") the Holy Office and moderating "its juridical rigor and assigning it a more positive and pastoral method." Paul VI restructured the Holy Office in a Motu Proprio entitled *Integrae servandae* dated December 7, 1965. This would lead to a renewal of the Church's system of censorship. The article then interprets *Integrae servandae* saying since the Index was not mentioned, the logical deduction was the Index would no longer continue to exist as a living document.

A key point to the article can be found when it states the *duty* remains for the faithful not to read matter contrary to faith and morals and that to go willfully against this is a sin. "Willfully," means that there are degrees of culpability and some actions are done innocently as opposed to maliciously. The Index was no longer in force, but the moral law remained and books about alleged private revelations are not exempt from it. After treating various other areas of discussion, the article then provides a brief note about how to bring a judgment of the Church against a particular writing to the attention of the clergy and the faithful. The article is content to say that the creation of a proper organ for this purpose was still underway at that time.[156] Certainly the advent of the Internet has made this task extremely easy.

At the end of the article there is a final appeal to man's rationality on the issue of the press and the Church and a further call for the faithful to take a pastoral approach to dialogue. History will judge whether or not this hope came true. The document is signed "P.", which could be P. Parente, the Secretary to the CDF at the time.

The English translation of this article was done by Miss Bistra Pishtiyska-McCullough with assistance by Mr. Matthew Sherry of St. Louis, MO.

Italian Text:

Le nuove disposizioni
per la tutela della Fede e della morale
nelle manifestazioni della stampa[1]

La Chiesa, fin dai primi secoli, ha sentito sempre il dovere di tutelare la fede e la morale dei suoi figli, secondo il divino mandato del suo Fondatore, che le ha affidato la missione di realizzare nel mondo il Regno di Dio per la salvezza di tutti.

La storia della Chiesa e contrassegnata dalla lotta contro gli errori teorici e pratici per assicurare l'integrità della fede e dei costumi.

Ma con la scoperta della stampa si diffuse maggiornmente il pericolo e la Chiesa fu costretta a ricorrere a mezzi più efficaci per la difesa.

Nacque così l'*Indice* dei libri proibiti che per quattro secoli è stato lo strumento di controllo e di difesa contro gli errori della stampa. Strumento utile ma sempre meno adeguato di fronte alla crescente mole delle pubblicazioni.

Oggi il voler seguire la stampa mondiale per un giudizio di valutazione delle singole opere e per un elenco esatto di quelle dannose o pericolose per la fede e i costumi, sarebbe un'impresa assai difficile, anche per il mutato clima psicologico individuale e sociale.

Il Sommo Pontefice Paolo VI, felicemente regnante, che al rispetto e alla difesa del patrimonio dottrinale e morale del passato unisce saggiamente la sensibilità per i problemi della coscienza moderna, nel Motu Proprio <<*Integrae servandae*>> (7 dicembre 1965), tenendo conto anche del desiderio dei Padri conciliari, ha riformato la struttura e lo spirito dell'antica Congregazione del

1 At the beginning of the article, the Latin text of the June 14 Notification was provided. It is here omitted.—Author.

S. Uffizio, conservandone il compito di vigilanza e di difesa per l'integrità della fede e dei costumi, ma moderandone il rigore giuridico e assegnandole un metodo più positivo e più pastorale.

Il Papa ha stabilito che la rinnovata Congregazione, prima di condannare un libro, si metta a contatto con l'Autore, si renda conto dell'ambiente, dove il libro è nato, ascoltando il parere dei Vescovi, e consideri la condanna formale come una *extrema ratio.*

Nel Documento Pontificio <<*Integrae servandae*>> non si fa menzione dell'*Indice*, che faceva parte della struttura del S. Uffizio; per conseguenza è da ritenersi che l'Indice, come tale, non continuerà più a vivere.

Intanto molti Vescovi hanno interpellato la S Sede sulla sorte dell'Indice: a queste giustificate domande risponde oggi la *Notificatio* pubblicata su questo giornale, a firma del Cardinale Pro-Prefetto della S. C. per la Dottrina della Fede, dietro approvazione del S. Padre.

La Notificazione dichiara anzitutto che l'*Indice* da oggi innanzi non ha più valore giuridico di legge ecclesiastica con le annesse sanzioni contro i libri proibiti e chi li legge, li conserva o li diffonde; ma rimane in pieno vigore il suo significato e il suo valore morale, nel senso che esso richiama ad ogni coscienza cristiana il dovere di evitare, anche secondo le esigenze del diritto naturale, la lettura dei libri pericolosi per la fede e i costumi.

Contravvenire deliberatamente a questo dovere è peccato, anche se non si incorre in una pena ecclesiastica.

Pertanto la Chiesa fa assegnamento sulla matura coscienza dei fedeli (lettori, autori, editori, educatori); ma soprattutto confida nella vigile opera dei Vescovi e delle Conferenze Episcopali, che hanno il diritto e il dovere di tutelare la fede e la morale dei loro sudditi, controllando, prevenendo e, se occorre, riprovando la cattiva stampa.

Il primo rimedio dunque è affidato ai Vescovi locali, che sono invitati ad agire di propria iniziativa, secondo le leggi della

Chiesa.

Al centro c'è la S. Congregazione per la Dottrina della Fede, la quale, alla luce del Motu Proprio <<*Integrae servandae*>> e delle direttive del Concilio Vaticano II, si metterà a contatto con l'Episcopato per aiutarne l'opera di controllo e di vigilanza sulla stampa.

Alla loro volta le Conferenze Episcopali mediante le proprie Commissioni dottrinali, collaboreranno e comunicheranno con la Congregazione per la Dottrina della Fede, che approfitterà anche delle ricche risorse delle Università ed altri Istituti Cattolici di cultura.

In tal modo la S. Sede e l'Episcopato agiranno efficacemente in armonia di propositi per arginare i pericoli e promuovere la sana dottrina.

Ma allora non ci saranno più condanne solenni come quelle della messa all'indice di una volta?

La Notificatione ammonisce che la S. Sede, secondo le esigenze della legge naturale e del mandato divino, si riserva il diritto di condannare pubblicamente un libro che offende la fede e i buoni costumi, ma non lo farà se non dopo di avere invitato benevolmente l'autore ad emendare il libro e l'autore si sia rifiutato di farlo.

Resta il problema di portare a conoscenza del Clero e dei fedeli il giudizio della Autorità Ecclesiastica sulle pubblicazioni di stampa e sulle correnti di pensiero nei vari Paesi.

A questa esigenza si provvederà con un organo di informationi a stampa, che è allo studio.

Ogni benpensante saprà apprezzare il nuovo atteggiamento della Chiesa di fronte alla stampa, ispirato non solo, come è giusto, all'immutabile dovere di tutelare la fede e la morale, ma anche al clima maturato nel Concilio, che modera l'impero della legge e dell'autorità con la fiducia nella coscienza e nel senso di responsabilità dei fedeli e col tono pastorale del colloquio e della persuasione.

P.

English Translation:

The New Dispositions
For the Protection of Faith and Morals in
Written Publications

From the beginning, the Church has always felt the duty to defend/protect the faith and the morality of her children, according to the Divine mandate of Her Founder Who has entrusted her with the mission to bring about the Kingdom of God in the world for the salvation of all.

The history of the Church is marked by struggle against theoretical and practical errors to ensure the integrity of faith and morals.

With the invention of the printing press, the danger spread even more and the Church was forced to turn to more effective means for defense.

For this reason, the Index of Prohibited Books came about, which for four centuries had remained the instrument of supervision and defense against the errors of the press. It was a useful instrument but less and less adequate in the face of the growing volume of publications.

Today the goal of following the world press in search of a judgment in order to evaluate individual works and make a detailed or precise list of those harmful or dangerous for faith and morals, would be a quite difficult endeavor in part because of the changed individual, social and psychological climate.

The Supreme Pontiff Paul VI, happily ruling, who both defends the moral and doctrinal heritage of the past and is sensitive to the problems of the modern conscience in the Motu Proprio <<*Integrae servandae*>> (7 December 1965); also, partly in view of the desire of the Council fathers, has reformed the structure and the spirit of the old Congregation of the Holy Office, thus preserving its task of vigilance and defense of the integrity of faith and morals, but moderating its juridical rigor and assigning it a more positive and pastoral method.

The Pope has established that the renewed Congregation, before condemning a book, should contact the author, to get information about the environment in which the book was written [emerged], should listen to the opinion of the Bishops, and should consider the formal sentence [condanna] as an *extrema ratio*. [extreme measure/last resort]

In the Pontifical Document <<*Integrae servandae*>> there is no mention of the Index, which belonged to the structure of the Holy Office; consequently, it should be deduced that the Index, as such, will not continue to exist anymore.

Meanwhile many Bishops have consulted the Holy See on the fate of the Index: these justified questions are answered in the *Notification* published today in this newspaper, signed by the Cardinal Pro-Prefect of the Sacred Congregation for the Doctrine of the Faith, with the approval of the Holy Father.

The *Notification* declares first of all that starting today the Index does not have juridical value of ecclesiastical law anymore with the related penalties [sanctions] against the prohibited books and against those who read, possess or spread them; but its [the Index] meaning and its moral value remain in full vigor [effect], in the sense that it reminds every Christian conscience of the duty to avoid, also according to the demands of the natural law, reading of books that are dangerous for faith and morals.

Contravening this duty willfully is a sin, even if it does not incur an ecclesiastical punishment.

Therefore the Church relies on the mature conscience of the faithful (readers, authors, publishers, educators); but above all it confides in the watchful work of the Bishops and the Episcopal Conferences, who have the right and the duty to protect the faith and morals of their subjects [the faithful], monitoring, preventing and, if necessary, admonishing the bad press.

Accordingly, the first remedy is entrusted to the local Bishops, who are invited to act of their own initiative according to the laws of the Church.

In the center is the Sacred Congregation for the Doctrine of the Faith, which, in the light of the Motu Proprio <<*Integrae servandae*>> and of the directives of Vatican II, will contact the Bishops to assist their work of control and vigilance over the press.

For their part, the Episcopal Conferences, through their own doctrinal Commissions, will work and communicate with the Congregation for the Doctrine of the Faith, which will also take advantage of the rich resources of the Universities and other Catholic Institutes of culture.

In this way the Holy See and the Bishops will effectively act in harmony of intentions in order to reduce the dangers and promote proper [sound] doctrine.

But does this mean there will be no more solemn condemnations like the former practice of placing publications on the Index?

The *Notification* admonishes that the Holy See, according to the demands of the natural law and divine mandate, reserves to itself the right to condemn publicly a book that offends the faith and good morals, but it will not do so before benevolently inviting the author to amend the book and unless the author refuses to do so.

There still remains the problem of informing the clergy and faithful about the judgment of Ecclesiastical Authority, about press publications and about the trends of thought in the various countries.

In order to resolve this, planning is underway for an information office to meet this need.

Every reasonable person will be able to appreciate the new attitude of the Church with respect toward the press, which is inspired not only, and justly so, by the immutable duty to protect faith and morals, but also by the climate matured at the Council [outlook developed at the Council], which moderates the rule of law and authority with confidence in the conscience and in the sense of responsibility of the faithful and with a pastoral tone of dialogue and persuasion.

P.

—APPENDIX E—

Decree *Post editam*
Congregation for the Doctrine of the Faith
November 15, 1966

Introduction:

After the change in the condition of the Index of Forbidden Books in June of 1966, a canonical question arose concerning canons 1399 and 2318 of the 1917 CIC. These canons concerned the prohibition of books that did not receive canonical approval (1399) and commensurate censures (2318). Specific types of books were listed and among them were [alleged] private revelations in §5 of canon 1399, which read as follows:

Canon 1399 §5 (Latin Text):

> Ipso iure prohibentur:
> Libri de quibus in can. 1385, §, n. I et can. 1391; itemque ex illis de quibus in cit. can. 1385, §I, n. 2, libri ac libelli qui novas apparitiones, revelationes, visiones, prophetias, miracula enarrant, vel qui novas inducunt devotiones, etiam sub praetextu quod sint privatae, si

> editi fuerint non servatis canonum praescriptionibus.

English translation:

> By law are forbidden:
> ...books and booklets which narrate new apparitions, revelations, visions, prophecies, miracles or aim to introduce new devotions, even though they pretend to be purely private, i.e., without complying with the law of previous censorship.[157]

It is clear anything concerning alleged private revelations could not be published without prior censorship. That censorship was outlined in Canon 1385, which, it should be noted, was not abrogated in *Post Editam*.[158]

The unique aspect of canons 1399 and 2318 that must be pointed out is their legality was rooted in the force of law that the Index enjoyed prior to June 14, 1966. Once the Index was no longer lawfully binding upon Catholics (though it retained its moral character and force), the natural result was to question the legality of canons 1399 and 2318.

The above question was put to the CDF. The congregation responded in a decree entitled *Post Editam* (PE) of November 1966, decreeing canons 1399 and 2318 were abrogated as the Index no longer enjoyed the force of law. The hypothesis Catholics could now lawfully disseminate materials on alleged private revelations arose some time after and quickly took root in the minds and hearts of numerous Catholics. The reasons for this are a matter for historical conjecture.

As with PLA, PE is re-presented in order to see the documents again and decide if the hypothesis is true. Combined with subsequent historical developments discussed in this book, Catholics may now see the documents in a context of consistent Magisterial teaching. The "pedagogy" formed by this consistency is tantamount in understanding the mind of Rome on the question of the Church and the publication of books on alleged private revelations. PE is translated by Dr. Michael Woodward.

Latin Text:
Acta Apostolicae Sedis, Volume 58, 1966, page 1186:

ACTA
SS. Congregationum Sacra Congregatio pro Doctrina Fidei

Decretum

POST EDITAM <<Notificationem>> diei 14 junii c. a. circa <<Indicem>> librorum prohibitorum, quaesitum fuit ab hac S. Congregatione pro Doctrina Fidei an in suo vigore permaneat can. 1399, quo quidam libri ipso iuri prohibentur, et can. 2318, quo quaedam poenae feruntur in violatores legume de censura et prohibitione librorum.

Dubiis in plenario conventu fer. IV diei 12 Octobris 1966 propositis, Emi Patres rebus Fidei tutandis praepositi respondendum decreverunt:

1. Negative ad utrumque, quoad vim legis ecclesiasticae; iterum tamen inculcato valore legis moralis, quae omnino prohibit fidem ac bonos mores in discrimen adducere;
2. Eos vero, qui forte innodati fuerint censuris de quibus in can. 2318, ab iisdem absolutos habendos esse ipso facto abrogationis eiusdem canonis.

Et in Audientia Emo Cardinali Pro-Praefecto S. Congregationis pro Doctrina Fidei die 14 eiusdem mensis et anni concessa, praefatum decretum S. Pontifex Paulus Papa VI benigne adprobare dignatus est ei publici iuris fieri mandavit.

Datum Romae, ex aedibus S. Congregationis pro Doctrina Fidei, die 15 novembris 1966.

A. Card. OTTAVIANI
Pro-Praefectus

+ P. Parente
Secretarius

English Translation:

ACTS
of the Sacred Congregation for the Doctrine of the Faith

Decree

AFTER the "Notification" was published on the 14th day of June of this year concerning the Index of Forbidden Books, it was asked by this Holy Congregation for the Doctrine of the Faith whether two canons remain in force: Canon 1399, whereby certain books are prohibited by right, and Canon 2318, whereby certain penalties are brought against violators of the laws concerning the censure and prohibition of books.

To the questions proposed in the full council on Wednesday, the 12th day of October, 1966, the most eminent Fathers, who are entrusted to respond in matters of protecting the faith, decreed:

1. Negatively to both, insofar as the power of ecclesiastical law; yet nevertheless with the validity of the moral law in force, which completely forbids bringing faith and good morals into peril;
2. And that those who perhaps were bound by the censures in Canon 2318 are held absolved from them by virtue of the abrogation of the same canon.

And in an audience with the most eminent Cardinal, Pro-Prefect of the Sacred Congregation for the Doctrine of the Faith, granted on the 14th day of the same month and year, the Holy Pontiff, Pope Paul VI, kindly deigned to approve the above decree and ordered it to be made public law.

Given at Rome, from the office of the Sacred Congregation for the Doctrine of the Faith, on the 15th day of November, 1966.

A. Cardinal OTTAVIANI
Pro-Prefect

+ P. Parente
Secretary

—APPENDIX F—

1996 *Press Release*
Congregation for the Doctrine of the Faith
December 4, 1996

Introduction:

The 1917 CIC specified books on miracles, revelations, etc. were required *by law* to undergo censorship. In the 1983 CIC, the new canons on censorship reflect the change in the Church's system of censorship, as they do not contain censures against those who disseminate matter contrary to faith and morals. Canon 823 in particular upholds the right of the Pastors of the Church to demand writings which touch upon faith and morals be submitted to their judgment. The canon reads:

> § 1. In order to preserve the integrity of the truths of faith and morals, the Pastors of the Church have the duty [*officium*] and right [*ius*] to be watchful so that no harm is done to the faith or morals of the Christian faithful through writings or the use of instruments of social communication. They also have the duty and right to demand that writings

> to be published by the Christian faithful which touch upon faith or morals be submitted to their judgment and have the duty and right to condemn writings which harm correct faith or good morals.
>
> § 2. Bishops, individually or gathered in particular councils or conferences of bishops, have the duty and right mentioned in §1 with regard to the Christian faithful entrusted to their care; the supreme authority of the Church, however, has this duty and right with regard to the entire people of God.[159]

The canon is written to highlight the rights of bishops to censor materials touching upon faith and morals. However, even though it speaks of the "duty" [*officium*] of the bishops, the canon is not written to accentuate the *moral imperative/force* behind the canon. If it were, the canon would include emphatic terms such as *must* or *ought to* demand. To do this, however, would come dangerously close to forcing the faithful by precept, something Pope Paul VI did not want. As a result, the moral force behind the canon is relegated to the background in favor of the right of the bishops to apply censorship.

The Code leaves the particular enforcing of the law to the discretion of the bishops as to when and how to exercise their right of censorship.[160] Canon 823 allows Ecclesiastical Authority to require writings related to faith and morals be submitted to prior censorship.[161] It is left to particular law to determine which books require prior censorship.[162] The "vigilance" required for such an undertaking is considerable, especially in view of the vast modern means of social communication. This is also why the faithful must maintain unity with their bishop(s) and assist him in regard to censorship.

The obligation of censorship forces the bishops to be vigilant regarding the materials being published in their dioceses or being written by the faithful of the diocese. This vigilance requires a vigorous and well-maintained system of censorship.[163] It is within this canonical and moral context PR is to be understood. If removed from this context, the law becomes dangerously close to allowing morality to become separated from religion and this is a most dangerous error.[164]

In PR, the CDF re-established an important theological premise: materials on alleged private revelations are connected to faith and morals and thus fall under censorship as specified in canon 823 §1 of the 1983 CIC. In practical terms this means under the moral law, such materials should be submitted to the Pastors of the Church for their censorship *before* the materials are printed and disseminated. It also means the Pastors of the Church can demand it without the faithful requesting it.

All of the above raises another question: are the *imprimatur* and *nihil obstat* necessary for materials on alleged private revelations? The CDF's press release does not say they are a *necessary legal* pre-requisite for publication as they once were under the 1917 CIC. Hence the question is disputed, especially given the "permission" and "approval" language of the 1983 CIC as based in EP.

However one answers the question, there is one indisputable fact—censorship itself *is morally required* for materials on alleged private revelation. The faithful are expected to comply with the moral law in order to be Catholics in good standing. Failure in this regard is a moral shortcoming that needs to be corrected, lest these sobering words from Christ be heard, "*Depart from Me, ye accursed of My Father…for I never knew you*" (Matthew 25:41).

The CDF's 1996 Press Release: Congregation for the Doctrine of the Faith Issues Press Release on Ryden Notification

I. The Congregation for the Doctrine of the Faith has received various questions about the value and authority of its Notification of 6 October 1995, published in L'*Osservatore Romano* on Monday/Tuesday, 23/24 October 1995, p. 2 (L'*Osservatore Romano* English edition 25 October 1995, p. 12), regarding the writings and messages of Mrs. Vassula Ryden attributed to alleged revelations and disseminated in Catholic circles throughout the world.

In this regard, the Congregation wishes to state:

1. The Notification addressed to the Pastors and faithful of the Catholic Church retains all its force. It was approved by the competent authorities and will be published in *Acta Apostolicæ Sedis*, the official organ of the Holy See, with the signatures of the Prefect and the Secretary of the Congregation.
2. Regarding the reports circulated by some news media concerning a restrictive interpretation of this Notification, given by His Eminence the Cardinal Prefect in a private conversation with a group of people to whom he granted an audience in Guadalajara, Mexico, on 10 May 1996, the same Cardinal Prefect wishes to state:
   a. as he said, the faithful are not to regard the messages of Vassula Ryden as divine revelations, but only as her personal meditations.
   b. these meditations, as the Notification explained, include, along with positive aspects, elements that are negative in the light of Catholic doctrine:
   c. therefore, Pastors and the faithful are asked to exercise serious spiritual discernment in this matter and to preserve the purity of the faith, morals and spiritual life, not by relying on alleged revelations but by following the revealed Word of God and the directives of the Church's Magisterium.

II. Regarding the circulation of texts of alleged private revelations, the Congregation states:

1. The interpretation given by some individuals to a Decision approved by Paul VI on 14 October 1966 and promulgated on 15 November of that year, in virtue of which writings and messages resulting from alleged revelations could be freely circulated in the Church, is absolutely groundless. This decision actually referred to the "Abolition of the Index of Forbidden Books," and determined that—after the relevant censures were lifted—the moral obligation still remained of not circulating or reading those writings which endanger faith and morals.
2. It should be recalled however that with regard to the circulation of texts of alleged private revelations, canon 823 §1 of the current Code remains in force "the Pastors of the Church have the right to demand that writings to be published by the Christian faithful which touch upon faith or morals be submitted to their judgment."
3. Alleged supernatural revelations and writings concerning them are submitted in first instance to the judgment of the Diocesan Bishop, and, in particular cases, to the judgment of the Episcopal Conference and the Congregation for the Doctrine of the Faith.

—ENDNOTES—

1 Reginald Garrigou-Lagrange, *The Three Ages of the Interior Life*. Volume II. (Rockford, Illinois: TAN Books, 1989), 580. Hereafter Garrigou-Lagrange followed by volume and page number. See also the Second Vatican Council's *Constitution on Divine Revelation (Dei Verbum)*, paragraph 4.

2 Congregation for the Doctrine of the Faith, *The Message of Fatima*. Published in Tarcisio Bertone, *The Last Secret of Fatima* (New York: Doubleday, 2008), 141. Hereafter Bertone followed by page number. There is some debate as to what "private" means. Some theologians, such as Garrigou-Lagrange (see endnote 1), restrict the term to mean those revelations intended for private individuals. Others broaden the term to distinguish such revelations from "public/divine" revelation. Cf. De Letter (contrib.), *The New Catholic Encyclopedia*, Volume XII. (New York: The Catholic University of America, 1967), 447. Bertone, 141 seems to indicate the Vatican has settled the debate in favor of the broader interpretation.

3 See Bertone, 143.

[4] 1 John 4:1-2.

[5] Joachim Bouflet and Philippe Boutry, Un signe dans le ciel (Paris: Grasset, 1997), 396-99.

[6] The full title of the document is *Normae S. Congregationis pro doctrina fidei de modo procedendi in diudicandis praesumptis apparitionibus ac revelationibus* (hereafter NC). This is translated literally as, "Norms of the Sacred Congregation for the Doctrine of the Faith on Modes of Procedure in Judging Presumed Apparitions and Revelations." The document was released by the Vatican in May, 2012 and is available on the Holy See's website:

<http://www.vatican.va/roman_curia/congregations/cfaith/documents/rc_con_cfaith_doc_19780225_norme-apparizioni_en.html> (Accessed 23 May, 2012).

[7] NC, III:1 through III:3 and IV: 1-2.

[8] Ibid., Preliminary Note 2a through 2c.

[9] Ibid., I:B:a. to I:B:e.

[10] Ibid., I:A:a. to I:A:3.

[11] I am indebted to Fr. Andrew Kingham who wrote his Ph.D. dissertation on NC in 2007 for the University of Ottawa. He provided much clarity on this aspect of the negative criteria on page 132 of his dissertation.

[12] On this point, NC references St. Ignatius of Loyola's *Spiritual Exercises* n.336. After some modest research, I believe the number 336 may correspond to an older reference system of the *Exercises* for the last paragraph (#8) of the second week of the discernment of spirits. See St. Ignatius of Loyola, *Manresa: Or the Spiritual Exercises of St. Ignatius* (London: Burns and Oats Lim-

ited, year unknown), 270. For a summary of the matter as it pertains to the spiritual life and extraordinary mystical phenomena, cf. Antonio Royo, O.P., and Jordan Aumann, O.P., *The Theology of Christian Perfection* (Dubuque: The Priory Press, 1962), 629. Hereafter Royo & Aumann followed by page number.

13 This is closely related to questions about the fruit (see questions 184-192).

14 NC, I:B:e.

15 Fr. Manfred Hauke discusses the discernment process and the role of miracles in his book *Introduzione alla Mariologia (Collana di Mariologia 2*), (EuPress FTL: Lugano Switzerland, 2008, 303-329. He discusses a distinction between "internal" and "external" criteria, and states NC is "predominantly" concerned with "internal" criteria. This is an important discussion on the role of miracles in the discernment of a case, but it is not an area much considered or explored in this book. It suffices to say the miracle, as Hauke points out, must have an undeniable connection with the alleged apparition and be rigorously investigated so as to ascertain whether or not any other explanation exists for the event.

16 Bertone, 143. See also Galatians 1:6-9 and John 17:11. In paragraph 14 of his Post-Synodal Apostolic Exhortation, *Verbum Domini*, Pope Benedict XVI reiterated this teaching, the text of which is on the Holy See's website:

<http://www.vatican.va/holy_father/benedict_xvi/apost_exhortations/documents/hf_ben-xvi_exh_20100930_verbum-domini_en.html> (Accessed December 4, 2010) [Hereafter VD followed by paragraph number].

17 NC, III:2-3. The twenty-fifth session of the Council of Trent decreed a bishop could have recourse to a provincial council and await a sentence from the metropolitan and other bishops of the

province in consultation with the Roman Pontiff. This was in matters of relics and alleged miracles (alleged apparitions and visions following in tandem). This appeals provision has for all intents and purposes fallen into abeyance since Vatican II, the advent of the conferences of bishops, and the promulgation of the 1983 *Code of Canon Law* (hereafter 1983 CIC). For more on the conferences, confer with the Second Vatican Council's Decree *Christus Dominus* paragraphs 36-37. Hereafter CD followed by paragraph number.

[18] NC, II:1-4 & III:1.

[19] Canon 134 of Canon Law Society of America, *Code of Canon Law*: Latin-English Edition. (Washington, D.C.: Canon Law Society of America, 1999), 124. Hereafter Code followed by canon number.

[20] NC, II:1-4.

[21] Ibid., II:3.

[22] Ibid. II:4.

[23] Ibid.

[24] *The Catholic Encyclopedia*, ed. Charles G. Herbermann (edit.), Volume XIV (New York: Robert Appleton Company, 1912), 336-337. See also Royo & Aumann, 636-639.

[25] Pope John Paul II, *The Catechism of the Catholic Church.* (Citta del Vaticano: Libreria Editrice Vaticana, 1997), paragraph 67. Hereafter CCC followed by paragraph number. There is some debate over whether or not the person receiving the alleged revelations is bound to believe them with Catholic faith versus those who are not receiving the alleged visions. Donald Attwater provides both positions in his, *A Dictionary of Mary* (New York: P.J. Kenedy & Sons, 1956), 246. Hereafter Attwater followed by page

number.

[26] VD, 14.

[27] Bertone, 140.

[28] Ibid., 142. See also VD, 14.

[29] Ibid. This citation quotes Cardinal Prospero Lambertini's (later Pope Benedict XIV) treatise entitled, *De Servorum Dei Beatificatione et Beatorum Canonizatione.* In 1852, a partial English translation appeared (in three volumes) of the Cardinal's treatise and was entitled, *Heroic Virtue: A Portion of the Treatise of Benedict XIV on the Beatification and Canonization of the Servants of God.* (London: Thomas Richardson and Sons, 1852). Hereafter Lambertini followed by volume and page number. Lambertini, Vol. 3, 395 has a slightly different translation than the one given in Bertone, 142. Both are to be compared with the original Latin found in paragraph 15 of Pope Benedict XIV, *De Servorum Dei Beatificatione et Beatorum Canonizatione Tomus III* (Prati: Alber et Ghettus Soc., 1840), 609.

[30] Bertone, 143. See also VD, 14.

[31] NC, III:3 & IV:1-2. It is also theoretically possible for the Vatican to intervene in non-serious cases in virtue of Rome's universal jurisdiction. However, this is not customary.

[32] Typically, Rome will become involved when it is specifically asked to intervene.

[33] The eleventh session of the Fifth Lateran Council (19 December 1516) did state private inspirations were to be examined by the Apostolic See before publication. However, this is not the current legislation as given in NC.

[34] NC, IV:1:b.

35 *Acta Apostolicae Sedis*, Volume 87, 1996, pages 956-957 (hereafter AAS followed by volume, year and page number). In this case, the claimant had no Catholic bishop and the significant notoriety surrounding the case caused the Congregation for the Doctrine of the Faith (hereafter CDF) to act on its own authority. I am making no personal statement about this particular claim of private revelations. See also AAS 26 (1934), 433 and AAS 43 (1951), 561-562 for examples of how Rome has acted towards alleged private revelations prior to NC.

36 Cf. NC, III:1-3.

37 Ibid., III:2:a-b.

38 Cf. section IV of Msgr. Charles Scicluna's essay, *Orientamenti dottrinali e competenze del vescovo diocesano e della Congregazione per la Dottrina della Fede nel discernimento delle apparizioni mariane*. "Pontificia Academia Mariana Internationalis", Apparitiones Beatae Mariae Virginis in Historia, Fide, Teologia. Acta Congressus marioligici-mariani internationalis in Civitate Lourdes Anno 2008 celebrati. Studia in sessionibus plenaria exhibita, vol 1, PAMI, Città del Vaticano 2010, 329-356. Hereafter Scicluna Essay.

39 Cf. NC, III:2:a.

40 Code, 139.

41 This is without prejudice to cases where someone's writings were altered by someone else. The most celebrated case of this in recent history is Bl. Anne Catherine Emmerich.

42 Cf. NC, I:B:d.

43 AAS, 7 (1915), 594. See also AAS, 8 (1916), 175.

44 In 1992, the CDF issued a document entitled, *Instruction on Some Aspects of the Use of the Instruments of Social Communication in Promoting the Doctrine of the Faith.* Section I:5:1-2 discusses "doctrinal commissions," though not in the context of alleged private revelations. This document is available on the Holy See's website:

<http://www.vatican.va/roman_curia/congregations/cfaith/documents/rc_con_cfaith_doc_19920330_istruzione-pccs_en.html> (Accessed 30 June, 2012). Hereafter SC 1992 followed by section number. It is customary for bishops to have investigatory commissions regarding alleged private revelations. Donal Anthony Foley in *Marian Apparitions, the Bible and the Modern World* argues that Session 25 of the Council of Trent, "*...set out the way Marian apparitions would be investigated in future*" (Emphasis mine). (Donal Anthony Foley, Marian Apparitions, The Bible and the Modern World. [Leominster: Gracewing Publishing, 2002], 49.) Foley's argument is based upon how the session made provision for a bishop to set up a commission of learned people to investigate relics, alleged miracles and such. The session said nothing specifically about alleged apparitions but such follows in tandem with relics and miracles.

45 Interestingly, NC (Preliminary Note, 2) lists only two of these judgments—*Constat de supernaturalitate* and *non constat de supernaturalitate.* There is no third "*constat de non supernaturalitate*" type. However, it is attested to in a letter written by Cardinal Bertone in 1997 to a French bishop in response to a dubium.

46 Though open to a more definitive judgment, "*non constat de supernaturalitate*" is still a negative category.

47 The CDF issued a letter clarifying a statement made by a

bishop on a specific claim in his diocese. Cardinal Bertone, who signed the letter as secretary of the Congregation, stated in a recent interview (Bertone, 92-96) the Congregation was asked to give a *clarification* of a *negative* opinion expressed by a bishop on a claim. The Congregation's response, however, was very clear—the opinion of the bishop in question was only an opinion and not an official judgment of events. Cardinal Bertone says nothing about the Holy See "overruling" the opinion.

[48] NC, II:2.

[49] Cf. Pope John Paul II, Post-Synodal Apostolic Letter *Christifideles Laici*, 20. Hereafter CL.

[50] The Second Vatican Council's Constitution on the Church "*Lumen Gentium*" (hereafter LG), 37 says:

The laity, like all the faithful, should be prompt to accept in a spirit of Christian obedience those decisions that the sacred Pastors make as teachers and governors of the church and as representatives of Christ; in doing so they follow the example of Christ, who by his obedience upon to death opened to all people the blessed way of the freedom of the children of God. (Translation in Norman P. Tanner, S.J., edit., *Decrees of the Ecumenical Councils, Volume II.* [Washington: Georgetown University Press, 1990], 879.) Hereafter Tanner followed by volume and page number.

The Latin text is as follows in Tanner:

[L]aici, sicut omnes christifideles, illa quae sacri Pastores, utpote Christum repraesentantes, tamquam magistri et rectores in Ecclesia statuunt, christiana oboedientia prompte amplectantur, Christi exemplum secuti, qui, sua oboedientia usque ad mortem, beatam libertatis filiorum Dei viam omnibus hominibus aperuit.

[51] NC, III:3.

[52] I am indebted to Msgr. Charles Scicluna's essay (section V) for providing clarification on this matter.

[53] For some excellent remarks in this regard, see Desmond A. Birch, *Trial Tribulation & Triumph: Before, During, and After Antichrist* (Santa Barbara: Queenship Publishing Company, 1996), 200.

[54] LG, 26, quoting St. Thomas Aquinas, teaches charity and unity of the Mystical Body is necessary for salvation. "In any community of the altar, under the sacred ministry of the bishop, there is made manifest the symbol of that charity and 'unity of the mystical Body without which there can be no salvation'" (Tanner, Vol. 2, 870). "*In quavis altaris communitate, sub Episcopi sacro ministerio, exhibetur symbolum illius caritatis et 'unitatis Corporis mystici, sine qua non potest esse salus.'*"

[55] Cf. Code, 381. See also CL, 30. In the latter, John Paul II states the faithful should be in communion with the Pope and the local bishop. For Catholics not in the diocese wherein an alleged private revelation is said to be taking place, it would be reasonable for them to ask: Why would I want to participate in alleged private revelations that the local bishop is against? The question regards the communion of the Church and the charity that binds the faithful together through the common bond of baptism.

[56] This forms an important point about the "fruits" born by an alleged private revelation. If the faithful are, by and large, disobeying the local Ordinary, that is considered to be "bad fruit."

[57] CD, 7 upheld the fact bishops should defend their brother bishops against slander.

[58] LG, 23 teaches every bishop has the duty to demonstrate solicitude for the faith even outside of his diocese (Tanner, Vol 2, 867). Though the discernment of alleged private revelations is not in this text, such discernment would fall under the category of safeguarding the unity of the faith.

[59] CCC, 1814.

[60] CCC, 144.

[61] Cf. Garrigou-Lagrange, Vol. 2, 581.

[62] CCC, 1826, 1 Corinthians 13:1-4.

[63] CCC, 1822.

[64] CCC, 1827.

[65] CCC, 2095.

[66] CCC, 2559 and the *Glossary* definition on page 882 of humility.

[67] Garrigou-Lagrange, Vol. 1, 454.

[68] Garrigou-Lagrange, Vol. 2, 117-118.

[69] CCC, 144.

[70] CCC, 1269.

[71] CCC, 1806.

[72] CCC, 2088.

[73] CCC, 1807.

[74] CCC, 1809.

[75] The virtue of obedience is important because it is by the obedience of faith the Church will be able to recognize the virtue

of faith in a soul. See St. Francis De Sales, *Introduction to the Devout Life*. John K. Ryan, trans. (New York: Doubleday, 1989), 154-155; St. Thomas Aquinas (*Summa Theologicae* II:II q. 186, a. 8) says of obedience, "*Dicendum quod votum obedientiae est praecipuum inter tria vota religionis*." The English reads, "The vow of obedience is the principal one of the three vows of religion…" (Thomas Gilby, O.P. , edit., *St. Thomas Aquinas Summa Theologiae*. Volume 47. [New York: McGraw-Hill Book Company, 1966], 132-133). Hereafter Blackfriars followed by volume and page numbers. The virtue of humility is closely associated with obedience. In speaking on the obedience of the Blessed Virgin, St. Francis de Sales wrote, "This virtue [obedience] is the inseparable companion of humility. One is never found without the other, for humility makes us submit to obedience" (Fr. Lewis S. Fiorelli, edit., *The Sermons of St. Francis de Sales on Our Lady*. [Rockford: TAN, 1985], 92).

[76] Dom Garrigou-Lagrange, provides much reasoning and insight on obedience (Garrigou-Lagrange, Vol. 2, 152). See also Royo & Aumann, 630 and 634.

[77] It is especially important, as shall be demonstrated from the upcoming questions and answers on "fruits." Adherence and obeying one's bishop is a fruit to be looked at. LG, 27 teaches: "The faithful must adhere to the bishop as the church does to Jesus Christ, and as Jesus Christ does to the Father, so that all things may agree together through unity and abound to the glory of God" ("*Fideles autem Episcopo adhaerere debent sicut Ecclesia Iesu Christo, et sicut Iesus Christus Patri, ut omnia per unitatem consentiant, et abundent in gloriam Dei.*") (Tanner, Vol. 2, 872).

[78] Cf. Garrigou-Lagrange, Vol. 2, 582.

[79] Fr. William Most, *Our Lady in Doctrine and Devotion*. Sec-

tion entitled, "*Appendix: Discernment of Spirits*" available at the Eternal Word Television Network's (EWTN) website:

<http://www.ewtn.com/library/THEOLOGY/MARY523.HTM> (Accessed March 4, 2009). Hereafter Most followed by section title.

80 Ibid.

81 AAS, 70 (1978), 350. The Vatican acted in this case only after the diocesan archbishop removed the objections.

82 NC, II:2.

83 See also Garrigou-Lagrange, Vol. 2, 580.

84 A bishop may also allow any writings to be disseminated but understood to be the results of one's personal meditations and not promoting the writings as alleged messages from heaven.

85 NC, II:2.

86 Cardinal John Carberry, *Mary Queen and Mother: Marian Pastoral Reflections*. (Boston: Daughters of St. Paul, 1979) 350. See also Attwater, 301 and LG 66.

87 LG, 25 reminds the faithful to respect, concur and adhere to the bishops when they are teaching in communion with the Roman Pontiff (Tanner, Vol. 2, 869).

88 The "response of the faithful" is not to be confused with the response the faithful gives to claims of private revelation that have "gone public" and attract much attention before any investigation.

89 NC, Preliminary Note: 1-2. Ideally, the faithful come to know of supposed private revelations only after they have gone through legitimate channels of authority for discernment. This will vary, however, in accordance with any phenomena said to be occurring

and how widely publicized they are.

[90] Code, 822.

[91] Anonymous, *Manual of Christian Doctrine*. (Philadelphia: John Joseph McVey, 1914), 171. Hereafter Manual followed by page number.

[92] Manual, 173.

[93] The Church does not micromanage her faithful in every action but instead calls upon their informed consciences.

[94] It is the responsibility of the faithful to know that if they participate in alleged private revelations before their supernatural character has been decided upon the faithful may be openly exposing themselves to materials harmful to faith and morals. This is a grave moral responsibility.

[95] Most, "*Appendix: Discernment of Spirits*" (Accessed March 4, 2009).

[96] Code, canon 220.

[97] This is not to say Pope Urban VIII never made the statement. What is being stated is no one has produced a citation proving he said it. Richard Salbato, managing editor of the website Unity Publishing, claims to have read the quote in its original context (<http://www.unitypublishing.com/answers.html> [Accessed February 5, 2009]). Regretfully, Salbato does not provide a citation and was unable to locate the source after I inquired after it.

[98] Canon 1399 §5. See also Rev. Timothy Hurley's very helpful book, *A Commentary on the Present Index Legislation* (New York: Benziger Brothers, 1908), 112-116.

[99] Certain means of social communication such as the radio and

television raise questions on the feasibility of censorship. How would the Church censor such things? The Church does not censor the medium, rather she places restrictions ("censors") upon *her* members (lay, religious or clerical). One can see this in canons 822-832 of the 1983 CIC.

[100] Censorship might run counter to contemporary North American and European conceptions that we may publish and produce anything and everything regarding literature, history, art, human behavior, etc. Yet the Pastors of the Church, who have been charged by Christ to defend the flock from error and spiritual danger, have the authority to make judgments on these matters.

[101] For instance, if the offensive material was in a book by a Catholic, the Church has the right and duty to mandate this son or daughter of the Church correct the error before the book goes to print.

[102] Though the given formal reason for the abrogation of canons 1399 and 2318 was the loss of the Index's legal force, it is also true the canons enjoyed the benefit of natural law, which was expressely upheld after the canons' abrogation. This is partly why the prohibition against reading bad books was classified as general law. It was not necessary to have a decree against a specific book or other writing for the faithful to be transgressing the moral law if they read the material. Rather, the Church in the 1917 *Code of Canon Law* forbade by general decree various classes of books, of which private revelation was a category. The Index was a tool the Church used to highlight offensive books but she could not render judgment on every book. For some general information, please see Rev. P.J. Lydon's, *Ready Answers in Canon Law: A Practical Summary of the Code for the Parish Clergy* (New York: Benziger Brothers, 1934), 91-92.

[103] In the newspaper L'*Osservatore della Domenica* (April 24, 1966), Cardinal Ottaviani, then Pro-Prefect of the CDF, stated, "The enormous contemporary production was not affected by the Index; this was not a result of bad will or carelessness, but because of the complete absence of an adequate organization, that would require such extensive resources that not even the new Congregation for the Doctrine of Faith could supply them" (translation by Miss Bistra Pishtiyska-McCullough of Vatican Radio with assistance by Mr. Matthew Sherry of St. Louis for the purposes of this book).

[104] For more on the legal aspect of this change in the condition of the Index, see St. Thomas Aquinas' *Summa Theologiae* I:II Q.97, a.1.

[105] AAS, 58 (1966), 445. See also Allen Kent, Harold Lancour, Jay E. Daily, William Z. Nasri (edits.), *Encyclopedia of Library and Information Science* Volume 11 (CRC Press, 1974), 304.

[106] This was explicitly taught in the article in the Vatican's newspaper, L'*Osservatore Romano* that accompanied the official promulgation of *Post Litteras Apostolicas* (hereafter PLA). See also Matthew 18:6, Mark 9:42, Luke 17:2.

[107] If the Vatican censors a theologian, for example, an immediate outcry of the Vatican being "oppressive," "authoritarian," or "stuck in the Middle Ages" often results. For an example of such accusations, see Hans Kung, *My Struggle for Freedom: Memoirs* (Continuum International Publishing Group, 2004). See also Joseph Cardinal Ratzinger, *The Nature and Mission of Theology: Approaches to Understanding Its Role in the Light of Present Controversy* (San Francisco: Ignatius Press, 1995), 101-118 (hereafter Ratzinger followed by page number). Incidentally,

Kung gives some discussion on the Index of Forbidden Books in relation to Cardinal Ottaviani on page 432 of the above-mentioned book. He mistakenly says PLA was issued on July 14 for PLA when it was June 14.

[108] Cardinal Ottaviani responded to this line of thought in L'*Osservatore della Domenica* (cited above). He said, "What powers have the bishops over Catholic writers and readers? Those that are given or recognized to them by canon law and the Council, as teachers of faith and responsible in their diocese. They should probably not make use of convictions except in very rare cases." (translation by Bistra Pishtiyska-McCullough and Matthew Sherry).

[109] 1 Thessalonians 5:19-22, Greek text. Emphasis mine. See also Ratzinger, 120.

[110] 1 Timothy 3:15, Greek text.

[111] In L'*Osservatore della Domenica* (cited above), Cardinal Ottaviani remarked on this point as follows, "In the Declaration on religious freedom [*Dignitatis Humanae*], the Decree on the apostolate of the laity [*Apostolicam Actuositatem*] and the Constitution <<The Church and the contemporary world>> [*Gaudium et Spes*], The Second Vatican Council has recognized a greater maturity in the Catholic laity and a greater role of responsibility in the Church, the Mystical Body of Christ" (translation by Bistra Pishtiyska-McCullough and Matthew Sherry).

[112] In his first Encyclical, *Ecclesiam Suam*, 21 (AAS, 56 [1964], 615-616), Pope Paul VI has some excellent remarks on the nature of the vigilance required by the bishops. It can be argued the language of PLA is taken right from the concepts employed in *Ecclesiam Suam*. An English translation is available on the Vati-

can's website but I have here used the paragraph numbers as given in the edition of *Ecclesiam Suam* entitled, *Paths of the Church: First Encyclical Letter of Pope Paul VI,* published by the National Catholic Welfare Conference, Washington, D.C.

113 AAS, 67 (1975), 281-284. An English translation of this document is available on the Vatican's website:

<http://www.vatican.va/roman_curia/congregations/cfaith/documents/rc_con_cfaith_doc_19750319_ecclesiae-pastorum_en.html> (Accessed 9 February, 2012).

114 The CDF published its Press Release in 1996 as a Notification in L'*Osservatore Romano*, Weekly (English) Edition December 4, 1996. The Congregation's 1996 Notification will be hereafter abbreviated as PR.

115 Eight years after its publication, almost the entire text of EP was placed in the 1983 CIC.

116 PR, II: 1. In addition, Cardinal Ottaviani remarked in L'*Osservatore della Domenica* (cited above), "Even after the suspension of the Index, the ethical obligations that recall the conscience of the faithful and their responsibility in facing the dangers for the belief and for the morality still remain" (translation by Bistra Pishtiyska-McCullough and Matthew Sherry).

117 The theory Catholics could disseminate books on alleged private revelations became so prominent the theory "overlooked" canon 823 §1 of the 1983 CIC. This is evidenced by the fact many books on alleged private revelations published after 1983 still contained the "abrogation disclaimer" of the old canons 1399 and 2318. For an example of the "abrogation disclaimer," see Michael Freze, *Voices, Visions and Apparitions*. (Huntington: Our Sunday Visitor Books, 1993), 3, 86, 122.

118 PR, II: 3. The Congregation was, in essence, basing itself in EP as given in canon 823 §1.

119 Code, 824 §1.

120 See also Ratzinger, 127.

121 In other words, many did not see the *imprimatur* and *nihil obstat* were not *legally* required of the faithful anymore and under pain of censure but they were still morally bound to seek them.

122 Pope Paul VI, *Address to the Holy Roman Rota.* February 4, 1977. There is a partial English translation available in the journal *The Jurist* Vol. 38 (1978), 211.

123 See footnote 33 of Garrigou-Lagrange, Vol. 2, 586.

124 Garrigou-Lagrange, Vol. 2, 245-246. For some recent thoughts on the process of discernment, Dr. Paul Thigpen gives some considerations in his book, *The Rapture Trap* (West Chester: Ascension Press, 2002), 229-236. On page 230, Dr. Thigpen seems to say the local Ordinary is not the foremost judge of alleged private revelations.

125 This teaching can be found in the writings of St. Thomas Aquinas in chapter 10 of his work, *Contra Retrahentes Homines a Religionis Ingressu* (hereafter CR followed by chapter number). The Latin is as follows:

Sciendum tamen, quod sicut a diabolo suggeritur vel etiam ab homine religionis introitus, per quem aliquis accedit ad Christum sequendum, talis suggestio efficaciam non habet, nisi interius attrahatur a Deo. Dicit enim Augustinus in libro *De praedestinatione sanctorum*, quod omnes sancti sunt docibiles Dei, non quia omnes ad Christum veniant, sed quia nemo aliter venit; et sic religionis propositum a quocumque suggeratur, a Deo est. (Stanislai

Eduardi Frette, edit., *Thomae Aquinatis: Opera Omnia.* Vol. 29. [Parisiis: Ludovicum Vives, Bibliopolam Editorem, 1876], 175.)

An older English translation of the above is as follows:

But it must be understood, that a suggestion to enter religious life, proceeding either from man or from Satan, has no efficacy, unless it be accompanied by the interior attraction of God. St. Augustine in his book *De Praedestinatione Sanctorum* says, "that all the saints are taught by God, not because all come to Christ, but because no one comes to him by any other means. Thus the desire to enter religion, from whomseover such suggestion may proceed, comes from God" (Fr. John Proctor, *An Apology for the Religious Orders* [London: Sands & Co, 1902], 436). See also Richard Butler, *Religious Vocation: An Unnecessary Mystery* (Rockford: TAN Books, 2005), 100.

[126] CR, 10. Where many people seem to have difficulty is the devil would, in essence, be defeating himself as the soul the devil suggested into the religious state or priesthood would be on a very good path to heaven. St. Thomas Aquinas, in CR 10, upholds the suggestion to enter the religious state is not harmful and is indeed beneficial. If the suggestion draws men to do other work of the devil, however, then there is a problem.

[127] Suggesting an individual to enter the religious state or priesthood could lead others to a greater falsehood (such as heresy) inherent within the alleged revelations. In short, *what better way to get good public relations for a work of the devil than the entering of individuals into the religious state or priesthood*?

[128] CR, 10. Aquinas was answering an objection about Satan transforming himself into an angel of light and deceiving people. Aquinas distinguishes the *desire* to enter religion from the *sugges-*

tion to enter religion. The former comes from God, says Aquinas, but the latter can come from other sources. For Aquinas' text, cf.:

<http://dhspriory.org/thomas/ContraRetrahentes.htm#10> (Accessed 21 February, 2012). See also St. Teresa of Avila as found in E. Allison Peers (trans), *The Interior Castle*, (New York: Image, 1989), 189. Hereafter *The Interior Castle* followed by page number.

[129] Matthew 7:16.

[130] For a longer listing of positive elements, see Royo & Aumann, 630-632.

[131] *The Interior Castle*, 184.

[132] It might be possible to state the tradition of the Church sees the "fruit" hold *pride of place* because Jesus Christ Himself spoke of fruits (Matthew 7:16). For some recent remarks related to the question of the primacy of spiritual fruit, see Joseph Cardinal Ratzinger, *God and the World.* (San Francisco: Ignatius Press, 2002), 289-290.

[133] One must also discern between good fruits and using good fruits as a synonym for "the end justifies the means."

[134] In a related teaching on whether the consequences of the external action increase the goodness or malice of the external action, St. Thomas Aquinas taught an evil act can not be made good and vice versa (*Summa Theologicae* I, II q. 20, a. 5). The Latin text, in its fullness, reads:

Sed contra, *eventus sequens non facit actum malum qui erat bonus, nec bonum qui erat malus*: puta si aliquis det eleemosynam pauperi, qua ille abutatur ad peccatum, nihil deperit ei qui eleemosynam facit. Et similiter, si aliquis patienter ferat injuriam sibi factam, non propter hoc excusatur ille qui fecit. Ergo eventus sequens non addit ad bonitatem vel malitiam actus (Emphasis mine). (Blackfriars, Vol. 18, p. 98.)

An English translation:

On the other hand *a good act does not become bad or a bad act good because of a subsequent event.* That a beggar misuses and sins with the alms given him detracts nothing from the generosity of the giver; so also if somebody patiently endures a wrong this offers no excuse for him who inflicts it. Therefore the subsequent event adds nothing to the good or bad of an action (Emphasis mine). (Blackfriars, Vol. 18, p. 99.)

[135] Matthew 18:20.

[136] While at a place said to be where private revelations are taking place, the faithful earnestly pray to God. This is a good occurrence as it provides, among other things, a witness of faith. Faith is a component of good fruit. Someone who may not believe or has fallen away from the faith might witness faith being put into practice and convert or be moved by this witness to go to Confession. In such a case, the grace of conversion does not derive from the alleged private revelations but from the community of the faithful gathered together in unity.

[137] CCC, 1806.

[138] "True good" is here used in reference to eternal salvation.

[139] Kieran Kavanaugh, O.C.D. and Otilio Rodriguez, O.C.D. (trans.), *The Collected Works of Saint John of the Cross, The Ascent of Mount Carmel, Book Two*, Chapter 22 section 12 (Washington: ICS Publications, 1991), 228. Hereafter Kavanaugh followed by page number. See also VD 14.

140 *The Interior Castle*, 190.

141 Kavanaugh, 223.

142 Ibid., 223-224.

143 Ibid., 224. A venial sin, is described in Scripture as "sin that does not lead to death" (James 1:5:17). The Catechism speaks of it as allowing "charity to subsist, even though it offends and weakens it [charity]" (CCC 1855).

144 Ibid., 223.

145 The Norms are taken from the website of the Holy See as cited earlier.

146 Lambertini wrote *De Servorum Dei* using *Sanctissimus* and *Coelestis*. The current process and legislation on beatifications and canonizations takes much of its structure from Lambertini. *Sanctissimus* and *Coelestis* would later influence the 1917 CIC (specifically canon 1387). For more on the 1917 CIC, see Rev. Stanislaus Woywod, O.F.M., *A Practical Commentary on the Code of Canon Law, Volume II*, (New York City: Joseph F. Wagner, Inc., 1957), 143.

147 Whether or not Pope St. Pius X meant *Sanctissimus* or *Coelestis* is unspecified in *Pascendi* 55. There is some conflicting information in the available documentation that frustrates finding a proper answer. All of the documents I was able to find speak of "Urban's Decree". *Pascendi* 55 speaks of Urban's *Declaration* (The Latin text of *Pascendi* reads "*declaratione*" as found in *Acta Sanctae Sedis*, Vol. XL, 1907, p. 649. Hereafter ASS followed by volume, year and page number).

148 I am basing the name upon the incipit of the document.

149 Cf., Floyd Anderson (edit.), *Council Daybook* Vatican II, Session 3 (Washington: National Catholic Welfare Conference, 1965), 189, 200. Hereafter Anderson followed by session and page number. Hans Kung wrote a book in 1960 entitled *Erneuerung als Ruf in die Einheit* wherein he outlined a "different program" for the Council than what the Roman Curia had in mind. His work also recommended the abolishing of the Index. For more on this, see Peter Hebblethwaite, *Pope John XXIII*, (New York: Doubleday and Company, Inc., 1985), 373-374. At the same time, there was also at least one call for the Index of Forbidden Books to remain with the caveat that the penalty of excommunication be lifted for those who read or retain such books in their possession (Cf., Anderson [3], 303).

150 An example of the rumors in the press can be found in: the *Los Angeles Times*, "Pope Abolishes Curia Office to Judge Writing". February 9, 1966, pg. 10. The British publication *The Tablet* (February 12, 1966, page 198), in its own reporting on the early rumors of the Index, went so far as to make its own prognostications.

151 *The Los Angeles Times* [April 21, 1966, pg. 28] and the *Washington Post* [April 21, 1966 pg. A17] both used the word "interview" where it was in fact inappropriate. Cardinal Ottaviani did not give an "interview" (understood as sitting down with a journalist and a recording device) with the publication.

There is a difference in dates between the L'*Osservatore della Domenica* article (April 24, 1966) and the articles mentioned above in the *Los Angeles Times* and the *Washington Post* (both April 21, 1966). Both of these articles reference Cardinal Ottaviani's remarks as given either on April 20 or April 21 yet the actual L'*Osservatore della Domenica* article is dated April 24.

This discrepancy is very likely due to a customary practice for journals and periodicals to be dated for a certain day but released prior to that date.

[152] *The Tablet* has no mention of the L'*Osservatore della Domenica* article in either its April, May or June 1966 editions. Though, curiously enough, *The Tablet* provides some discussion (April 23, 1966, pg. 486-487) of remarks Cardinal Ottaviani made in the weekly Milan publication *Gente*.

If *The Tablet*'s reporting on what the Cardinal's remarks were in *Gente* is reliable, the remarks are similar to the L'*Osservatore della Domenica* article, though even this article references the earlier *Gente* article. The publication *Gente* is extremely hard to locate and I was not able to find a copy of the article. Without checking the article's contents against *The Tablet*'s reporting on the article, I do not think it advisable to discuss (as if it were factual) what Cardinal Ottaviani is reported to have said in *Gente*.

[153] I here use the word "inherited" to elucidate the text of Cardinal Ottaviani. Earlier testimony of the Cardinal's point can be found in a document entitled *De Prohibitione Librorum* published in AAS 35 (1943), 144. See also *Pascendi Dominici Gregis* (ASS, 40 [1907], 643).

[154] The word "*conditione*" is to be found in the Latin subtitle on the CDF's page on the Vatican's web site. The Italian translation is "abolition" (of the Index). Canonically, the Latin language is the official language of the Church and so I render my terms from the Latin where possible. The exact reason for this difference is not clear. Nevertheless, the Index remains a part of Catholic life and practice as a reference point (or as Cardinal Ottaviani said, a "historical document") we can look back upon for catechetical purposes. We can reference the Index when instructing people

on their moral duty under natural law not to disseminate matter contrary to faith and morals.

155 L'*Osservatore Romano*, Year 106, Issue 136, page 1.

156 It could be argued this was later implemented with the document *Ratio Agendi* of which there was two versions (AAS, 63 [1971], 234-236 and AAS, 89 [1997], 830-835). The second version is available online at the Vatican's website:

<http://www.vatican.va/roman_curia/congregations/cfaith/documents/rc_con_cfaith_doc_19970629_ratio-agendi_en.html> (Accessed on February 23, 2009).

157 P. Chas. Augustine, O.S.B., *A Commentary on the New Code of Canon Law*, Volume VI. (St. Louis: B. Herder Book Co., 1923), 466, 471. "The law of previous censorship" referred to canon 1385, on the censorship of books, of which devotional books are a part. Alleged revelations and visions were understood to fall under this canon (cf. ibid., 436). Fr. Augustine specifically mentions a few examples of writings based upon alleged private revelations.

158 This is in contradistinction to the claim by Mariologist Fr. Rene Laurentin who stated canon 1385 was abrogated. See Anthony Buono (gen. edit.), *Dictionary of Mary*, (New Jersey: Catholic Book Publishing Co., 1997), 39. Canon 1385 later became a part of the 1983 CIC (specifically canons 824-825 and 827) as demonstrated in Dr. Edward Peters, *The 1917 Pio-Benedictine Code of Canon Law* (San Francisco: Ignatius Press, 2001), 466. On another note, canon 2318 of the 1917 CIC did not mention penalties for those who promoted alleged private revelations without permission from the bishop. Instead, it focused upon the excommunication of those who publish books (and unapproved

versions of the Scriptures) written by those who have apostasized or hold manifestly heretical opinions. While it is true alleged private revelations could be heretical and lead to schism or apostasy, canon 2318 did not pertain so much to alleged private revelations as it did to those who have apostatized or hold manifestly heretical opinions.

[159] Code, 267-268, canon 823.

[160] The rules are slightly different for clerics and religious (cf. canons 831 §2 and 832).

[161] Canon 823 presupposes natural and eternal law, to say nothing of catechesis and the informing of conscience, which is proper to the Church. In other words, the idea is bishops have properly catechized the faithful on their duty to submit any such writings for censorship. This is the essence of the "mature conscience" of the faithful as the Church informs consciences (weakened by sin) on natural and eternal law and the saving doctrines of Jesus Christ. Anyone who does not comply with proper Catholic morality—and law—on censorship, the bishop ought to demand the composition for censorship. This is when "vigilant solicitude" of the bishops is manifested in a clear and direct way. If the author(s) refuse, then it is the duty and right of the bishop(s) to "hinder," "censure," and "condemn" the work as PLA states.

[162] Ernest Caparros, Michel Theriault, Jean Thorn (edits.), *Code of Canon Law Annotated* [Woodridge: Midwest Theological Forum, 2004], 634. Leaving it to "particular law" runs dangerously close to having a vast conglomeration of different systems based upon the subjective interpretations of individual bishops. One must wonder where the unity of Catholic morality would be, especially when the theological tradition specifies books touching upon faith and morals ought to undergo censorship. This tradition

helps bishops interpret canon 823 of the 1983 CIC on what types of books/other materials undergo censorship (such as private revelation). Furthermore, the 1983 CIC states in canon 6§2, "Insofar as they repeat former law, the canons of this Code must be assessed also in accord with canonical tradition" (Code, 6).

[163] There is also a moral responsibility for bishops to keep vigilance on books coming into their dioceses from outside and which influence the faithful.

[164] Pope Pius XI explicitly condemns the separation of morality from religion (thus removing all basis for legislation) as an error in chapter 3 of his *Encyclical Caritate Christi Compulsi* (New York: The Paulist Press, 1932), 17.